The Talk of the Galaxy

Other books by Paul A. LaViolette

Earth Under Fire:
Humanity's Survival of the Apocalypse

Background reading for *The Talk of the Galaxy*.
Examines geological and astronomical evidence
for the superwave cataclysm and deciphers myths
conveying information about its occurrence.

Beyond the Big Bang:
Ancient Myth and the Science of Continuous Creation

Background reading for *The Talk of the Galaxy*.
Elaborates related time capsule messages
encoded in the zodiac and other esoteric lore.

Subquantum Kinetics: The Alchemy of Creation

An uplifting physics for the 21st century.

Also see our web page at
http://www.etheric.com/

THE TALK
OF THE
GALAXY

An ET Message for us?

PAUL A. LAVIOLETTE

Starlane Publications
Alexandria, VA

Published by Starlane Publications
Alexandria, VA

email: Starcode @ aol.com

Diagrams are by Paul A. LaViolette unless otherwise noted

ISBN 0-9642025-3-0
Library of Congress Catalog Card Number: 00-090252

Subjects: 1. Interstellar communication. 2. Pulsars. 3. Supernova
remnants. 4. Interstellar travel. 5. Unidentified flying objects.

Printed in the United States of America

Contents

Preface and Acknowledgments   vii

1. **The Pulsar Enigma**   1
   Discovery   1
   The Neutron Star Lighthouse Model   8
   ETI Beacons?   15

2. **A Galactic Message**   18
   The One-Radian Arrow   18
   Superluminal Space Travel   29
   Spaceflight Navigation   30
   Superluminal Communication   33

3. **One-Radian Marker Beacons**   36
   The Millisecond Pulsar   36
   The Eclipsing Binary Millisecond Pulsar   41

4. **The Galactic Imperative**   48
   Message in the Stars   48
   Galactic Superwaves   50

5. **Superwave Warning Beacons**   60
   The Crab and Vela Supernova Remnants   60
   Pulsars Are Not Made in Supernova Explosions   61
   Wave of Destruction   65
   The King and Queen of Pulsars   75

6. **Sky Maps of a Celestial Disaster**   81
   A Star Chart of the Sagitta Constellation?   81
   An Event Chronometer   84
   A Celestial Memorial to a Terrestrial Cataclysm   86
   A Superwave Shield?   93
   Cosmic Synchronicity   96

7. **Natural or Artificial**   100
   Lighthouse Trouble   100
   Signal Ordering Too Complex to Explain   110
   A "Low-tech" Particle Beam Communicator   120
   Field Engineered Stellar Cores as ETI Beacons   123

8. **Force Field Beaming Technology**   **128**
     Aerial Plasmoids   128
     Microwave Phase Conjugation   131
     Tesla Waves   135
     The Crop Circle Phenomenon   138
     An ETI Connection?   144
     Project Centaur   148
     Contact   149

**Appendix A: Galactic Distribution of Pulsars
with the Parkes Survey Included**   **152**

Appendix B: Ordered Complexity   **154**
     Pulses and Time-Averaged Pulse Profiles   154
     Pulse Modulation   158
     Pulse Drifting   160
     Mode Switching   164

Appendix C: Particle Beam Communicator Luminosity   **173**

Notes   **175**

Bibliography   **183**

Index   **18**

Preface

For decades SETI astronomers have been searching the sky for radio signals of extraterrestrial intelligence origin, but have found nothing. Perhaps the problem is that they were looking for the wrong type of signal. They have been seeking discrete frequency transmissions similar to terrestrial AM or FM radio signals. But there is no guarantee that another civilization would be using this particular method of communication. Broadband transmissions, covering the entire radio frequency spectrum, would be a more logical choice because they would be more easily detected regardless of which frequency one's radio telescope happened to be tuned to. Such broad band emission, called "synchrotron radiation," is readily produced by magnetically decelerating a beam of cosmic ray electrons. By arranging that the electrons track in a straight line as they decelerate, the synchrotron radiation can be confined to a narrow beam that has minimal decrease of its intensity over interstellar distances, thereby ensuring that the target civilization will be receiving a strong signal.

This kind of radio transmission essentially describes the signals that astronomers routinely observe coming from pulsars. In particular, there is considerable evidence to suggest that these signals are artificial. Indeed, they are the most complex ordered phenomenon known to astronomy, and to this date, they have not been adequately accounted for by any natural-cause model. The neutron star lighthouse model, for example, falls far short of this challenge. Many astronomers, though, will experience difficulty relinquishing the paradigm they have come to accept, even when confronted with its shortcomings.

In reading this book, keep in mind that several sets of relationships must be taken into account to fully understand the symbolic message that the pulsar network is conveying. One part ties in with another to form a complete picture. So it is helpful to contemplate these findings as a whole. Also it is useful to read the books *Earth Under Fire* and *Beyond the Big Bang* since they provide background material essential to understanding the pulsar message.

Acknowledgments

I would like to thank my father Fred and also Tom Valone for the long hours they both spent helping me edit this manuscript. I would also like to thank Joscelyn Godwin, Jackie Panting, my sister Mary, and mother Irene for their helpful comments on the manuscript, and Geri Davisson for her help as well.

Chapter 1

The Pulsar Enigma

One other thing it can be is an intelligent civilization attempting to communicate with other worlds, because everybody has said that's how you'd mark yourself. You do something that can't be done in nature. You make the pulse rate of a nearby pulsar exactly right, not deviating in the least year after year.

Frank Drake, 1974

Discovery

It was July of 1967. The world's first scintillation radio telescope had just been completed, a device that would allow astronomers to detect rapidly varying radio emissions coming from distant stars. Cambridge University graduate student Jocelyn Bell and her astronomy professor, Anthony Hewish, were making final adjustments to the field of radio aerials that lay stretched out across the English countryside. Little did they know that within a month Jocelyn would stumble upon one of the most important astronomical discoveries of the century. They had finished scanning an area of the sky located in the direction of the constellation of Vulpecula. Jocelyn was looking over the yards and yards of pen chart data that scrawled the signals from their antenna array and noticed something quite unusual. One of the radio sources whose radio signal twinkling they had been observing appeared to be emitting a steady series of radio pulses, or "beeps", each lasting a few hundredths of a second. Hewish at first dismissed the pulses as radio interference from a terrestrial source such as sparking from a passing automobile. The signal had faded and could not be detected on subsequent observations, but one night it reappeared. After several months of observation, seeing that the signal came from a fixed location in the sky, he became convinced that they had detected a new kind of astronomical source.

At the end of November, after obtaining a suitable fast-response chart recorder, they were able for the first time to get an accurate fix on the timing of the pulses. Six hours of observations had shown that the pulses had a very regular recurrence period of 1.33733 ±0.00001 seconds. Additional months of observation added two more decimal places to the precision of the source, and today we know its period to better than six parts per trillion, yielding a pulsation period of precisely 1.337301192269 ±0.000000000006 seconds per cycle! This discovery caused quite a stir among the project's scientists. Nothing like it had ever been seen before. It seemed to them that they may have detected signals being sent from an alien civilization. Months of careful observation had revealed that the radio source lay about two thousand light years away. The idea that the object was a radio beacon operated by extraterrestrial intelligence (ETI) was seriously considered since this was the first time in the history of astronomy that a source of such precise regularity had ever been encountered. In fact, they initially named this source LGM 1, the acronym "LGM" standing for "Little Green Men." [1]

Near the end of December Jocelyn discovered a second pulsating radio source in the constellation of Hydra which lay in an opposite part of the sky. This one, which had a period 1.2737635 seconds, was later christened LGM-2. With the discovery of this second source, the Cambridge astronomers began to doubt their ETI hypothesis. Since the two pulsars were found to be separated from one another by over 4000 light years, they figured that if they were ETI transmitters, they would necessarily have been built by different civilizations. But then it seemed to them very unlikely that more than one civilization would have chosen to communicate with us at this particular point in time and in addition use a similar method of sending precisely timed pulses.

Fearing they would be inundated with reporters if their discovery had become known to the public, the astronomers kept their find a tightly guarded secret until February when they submitted a paper about it to *Nature* magazine. [2] Their paper, however, avoided making an extraterrestrial intelligence (ETI) interpretation. Rather they proposed that these signals might be emitted from the surface of a highly dense compact star, such as a white dwarf or neutron star, that was expanding and contracting, dimming and brightening, in a very regular manner. A decision to stick to their initial ETI hypothesis would most assuredly have condemned them to attacks from skeptical colleagues and would very likely have jeopardized their chances of publishing their findings in refereed journals. Besides, their study had originally been designed to investigate natural astronomical phenomena, not search the skies for signs of extraterrestrial intelligence. In the following months, the Cambridge scientists discovered two other extremely regular pulsating sources with comparable periods of 0.253065 and 1.187911 seconds, duly named LGM 3 and 4. Later, when these sources became known as *pulsars*, the four became renamed as PSR 1919+21, PSR 0834+06, PSR 0950+08, and PSR 1133+16.*

Multiple-source ETI communication, however, would not be all that unusual if the signals were coming from several intercommunicating civilizations, forming a kind of Galactic "collective" or "commune." In such a case, the idea of several communicators being on line and using similar methods of transmission would seem rather plausible. Today many scientists interested in the "Search for Extraterrestrial Intelligence," an endeavor known as SETI, believe that such a Galactic commune could very well exist. For example, MIT radio astronomer Professor Alan Barrett was one scientist who in the early 1970's was quoted by the *New York Post* as having wondered whether pulsar signals *"might be part of a vast interstellar communications network which we have stumbled upon"*.[3] But, the idea of a communication collective had not received much discussion back in 1967 and so doubts arose.

Another reason why the Cambridge astronomers began to question their ETI hypothesis had to do with the way the radio signals were being sent. Rather than being transmitted at discrete frequencies like our own radio and television stations, pulsar transmissions covered a broad range of radio frequencies. Astronomers Robert Jastrow and M. Thomas, for example, reasoned as follows:

> If an extraterrestrial society were trying to signal other solar systems, its interstellar transmitter would require enormous power to send signals across the trillions of miles that separate every star from its neighbors. It would be wasteful, purposeless, and unintelligent to diffuse the power of the transmitter over a broad band of frequencies. The only feasible way to transmit would be to concentrate all available power at one frequency, as we do on earth when we broadcast radio and television programs.[4]

Nevertheless, the development of particle beam weapon technology during the 1980's brought us a step closer to realizing that

---

* PSR signifies "pulsating source of radio" and the numbers indicate the source's sky position as seen in 1950 AD (an added J would signify year 2000). The first four digits give hours and minutes of right ascension measured from west to east along the celestial equator and the last two give degrees of declination measured either north (+) or south (-) from the celestial equator. The celestial equator is the outward projection of the Earth's equator onto the celestial sphere.

Figure 1. An ETI particle-beam communicator device proposed by the Author which could be used to transmit pulsar-like radiation pulses to other civilizations in the Galaxy (see chapter 7 for further details).

broadband ETI communicators are not such a far fetched idea after all. With this technology it is possible for us today to build a space-based device capable of projecting an intense beam of high-energy electrons that would in turn generate a highly collimated laser-like radio wave beam. This particle beam communicator would consist of two main components: a particle accelerator and a particle beam modulator unit (see figure 1). The particle accelerator would produce a beam of high-energy electrons traveling at very close to the speed of light. The beam modulator would apply magnetic forces transverse to this particle beam causing its electrons to deflect slightly and to convert some of their forward kinetic energy into *synchrotron radiation*, electromagnetic wave emission that characteristically spans *a broad range of frequencies*.

Synchrotron radiation was first discovered in the early 1940's when physicists at the General Electric Research Laboratory in Schenectady, New York first powered up the Synchrotron, one of the world's first high-energy particle accelerators. During its operation, they noticed that a fascinating blue-white glow was radiating from the accelerator's high-energy electron beam. It was later found that this emission had a very broad spectrum that ranged from low energy radio and microwaves on up to high-energy ultraviolet and X-rays. Electrons traveling near the speed of light are known to emit this broadband radiation whenever they are magnetically deflected from their normal straight-line trajectories. Their high speed causes them to emit this radiation as a narrow conical beam aimed in their direction of travel (see figure 2).

Figure 2. Electrons traveling at near-speed-of-light "relativistic" velocities emit narrow cones of synchrotron radiation when they are magnetically deflected.

Although it was first discovered in the laboratory, synchrotron radiation was later found to be quite commonly produced in nature. Radio astronomers typically detect its presence wherever high-energy cosmic ray particles are being deflected by magnetic fields. It is detected coming from solar flare particles trapped in the Earth's Van Allen radiation belts, from cosmic ray electrons magnetically trapped in supernova remnants, and from the tremendously energetic cosmic ray barrages emitted from the luminous quasar-like cores of exploding galaxies.

The pulsed radio signals coming from pulsars have also been determined to consist of synchrotron radiation. In fact, by properly controlling its modulator unit, the particle beam communicator shown in figure 1 could be made to produce a synchrotron beam that would flash on and off and produce a signal very similar to that coming from a pulsar. Powered by a medium sized power plant that supplied on the order of 10 to 100 megawatts, this communicator could produce a beamed signal that even at distances of thousands of light years would have a strength similar to that coming from a pulsar. Additional details about how such a communicator might operate are given in chapter 7.

Given that it is possible for a technically advanced civilization to produce broadband pulsar-like signals, what would be some of the advantages for them to do so, as opposed to broadcasting discrete frequency transmissions? For one thing, a broadband signal would stand a better chance of being detected by a radio telescope. Such telescopes are normally designed to receive a jumble of radio signals covering a broad range of frequencies, as would normally come from naturally occurring radio sources in the sky. A radio station broadcasting a single frequency would become lost in the background noise resulting from the thousands of radio frequencies being received. On the other hand, a broadband signal, whose intensity was made to coherently vary over all of its frequencies, would more easily stand out and be detected, and it could be detected regardless of which part of the radio frequency spectrum an astronomer happened to be observing. If an ETI signal were instead being transmitted on a single radio frequency channel, an astronomer would need to have the good fortune to tune into that particular channel out of billions of available channels. It would be like trying to find a "needle" in a cosmic "haystack." This difficulty could be overcome by retrofitting radio telescopes with specialized electronic equipment capable of rapidly processing data gathered simultaneously from millions of discrete channels. In fact, such signal processing equipment is currently being used in the SETI program. But, it is not the kind of apparatus that observational astronomers would normally use in surveying the radio-emitting sky.

Broadband signal transmissions also have the advantage of providing the recipient civilization with a way of estimating the communicator's distance. Interstellar space is filled with a tenuous medium of unattached electrons which causes lower frequency radio waves to travel slightly slower than higher frequency waves. This effect is due to radio wave scattering and not to any change in the wave's velocity through space. The low-frequency radio waves from a communication pulse, then, would lag slightly behind the high-frequency waves coming from the same pulse (see figure 3). Consequently, the recipients of the pulsed message could determine the sender's distance simply by measuring the amount of this frequency-dependent time delay. Such distance ranging would not be possible if the sending civilization were transmitting signals only at one frequency. So in retrospect, it seems that some of the reasons that were once given for discounting the possibility that pulsar signals might be of ETI origin are really not so sound.

Nevertheless early searches for intelligent signals in space were conducted on the assumption that the transmissions would be of the discrete frequency type. The first such radio telescope search was carried out by astronomer Frank Drake in 1959 and 1960. This project, named OZMA, used the 26 meter radio antenna at the National Radio Astronomy Observatory in Green Bank, West Virginia to search for signals from the two closest sun-like stars, Tau Ceti and Epsilon Eridani. Figuring that ETI signals would be transmitted at a discrete frequency, they tuned their telescope to scan what they thought would be the most likely frequency, 1420.405 MHz, the 21

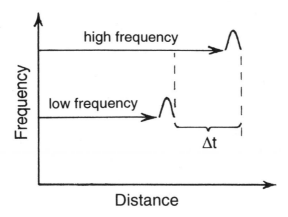

Figure 3. Compared with higher frequency radio waves, waves of lower frequency require more time to traverse the same distance through space. By measuring the amount of delay in radio pulse arrival time, astronomers are able to estimate the distance to the pulsating source.

centimeter line wavelength which atomic hydrogen normally radiates at. However, their search turned up nothing.

Although SETI enthusiasts carried out a variety of other searches in the years that followed, there was no organized scientifically recognized program at that time to fund such activities. Moreover during these early years, the scientific community was not nearly as tolerant as it is today of the idea that intelligent beings might live elsewhere in the Galaxy and might even be trying to communicate with us. It was not until 1984 that astronomers first came up with irrefutable observational evidence indicating the presence of solar systems around other stars. So, it is not surprising that back in 1967 Hewish and his Cambridge astronomy group had backed away from their ETI interpretation for pulsars.

The announcement of their findings created quite a stir in the astronomical community since no other natural sources were then known to exhibit such precisely timed pulses. It became regarded as one of the most important astronomical discoveries of the decade. Jocelyn Bell subsequently received considerable press recognition and Drs. Hewish and Ryle, who were co-directors of the Cambridge University radio telescope project, both shared the 1974 Nobel Prize in physics.

Shortly after the Cambridge pulsar findings were made public, other astronomers began their own searches. As a result, the number of known pulsars rose to 50 by mid 1970, then to 147 by 1975, 330 by 1981, 550 by 1992, to 706 by 1997, and by the end of the century their numbers had surpassed 1100. As many as 140 scientific papers were published on pulsars in 1968 alone, and hundreds more came out in the following years.

The Neutron Star Lighthouse Model

In the months after Hewish and Bell had published their pulsar discovery, scientists had come forth with as many as 20 different theoretical models attempting to explain the phenomenon. The earlier suggestion that pulsars might be radially pulsating white dwarf stars had to be discarded following the discovery later that year of two unusual pulsars found in the Crab and Vela supernova remnants. Both have periods under one tenth of a second, far too short to be realistically described by a radially pulsating dwarf star.

As an alternative, astronomers eventually settled on the "neutron star lighthouse model" which was proposed by Thomas Gold in June of 1968.[5] This conceived a pulsar to be an extremely dense, rapidly rotating mass of neutrons, called a *neutron star*, which was theorized to emit opposed beams of synchrotron radiation (see figure 4). With each rotation, one or both of these beams would sweep past the Earth producing a brief radio pulse

A neutron star is said to be formed when a star's fusion reactions burn out leaving the star's mass in free fall inward gravitational collapse. This compression is then said to be followed by a supernova explosion whose force further compacts the star's core. The result is theorized to be a state of matter so dense that all the star's nuclear particles have been transformed into neutrons and packed tightly together with the same density that exists in the nucleus of an atom. The star's core, which initially would have a mass somewhere between 1.2 to 3 times the mass of the Sun and a diameter about like that of the Earth, would become compressed to a size of only 1 to 30 kilometers. If it could be brought to the Earth's surface, one cubic centimeter of this substance would weigh somewhere between 25 million and one trillion tons!

The neutron star idea was first proposed in the 1930's. But for many decades thereafter, astrophysicists were not sure whether to believe that such things really existed. It was not until pulsars were discovered that they began taking the idea more seriously, since no

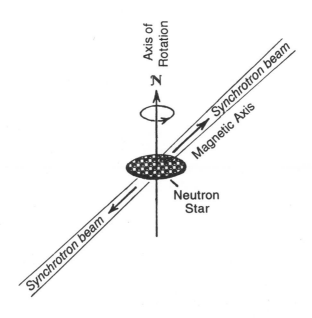

Figure 4. The lighthouse model proposed as an explanation of pulsar emission.

known natural object could explain pulsar signals. In their attempt to model pulsar signals, astrophysicists theorized that the neutron star would be spinning very rapidly, from several rpm up to hundreds of times per second, and that the resulting centrifugal forces would flatten it into the shape of a pancake.[6] Also it was thought that the star would be left with a magnetic field trillions of times stronger than the Earth's magnetic field. This would somehow be frozen into the neutron star matter itself and would be typically skewed at an angle to the star's axis of rotation.

Furthermore the neutron star was theorized to be left very hot as a result of its violent birth, its high temperature causing it to radiate a stream of high-energy electrons and other cosmic ray particles. These were thought to spew out from each of the star's magnetic poles to form two opposed pencil-like beams. One theory suggests that the star's magnetic field would decelerate these electrons as they rushed outward and in so doing would cause them to emit two collimated beams of synchrotron radiation, the same type of radiation produced by our hypothetical particle beam communicator. Since the beams were assumed to be oriented at an angle to the star's axis of rotation, they would sweep through space as the star revolved, much like searchlights from a rotating lighthouse beacon. If the Earth happened to be in the path of one, or in some cases both, of these beams, they would be observed to flash by with clock-like precision, producing a train of regularly spaced pulses.

There is, however, a fundamental problem with the neutron star lighthouse model. Whereas the model predicts that a pulsar's individual radio beeps should be evenly spaced from one another, instead *their arrival times are found to vary from one pulse to the next*. A typical example of pulse-to-pulse timing variation may be seen in figure 5 which charts a succession of pulses observed from pulsar PSR 0950+08. Each horizontal trace represents the signal received over a single pulse cycle, with 260 of these cycles being stacked up for comparison. The hump-like pulses consist of a rise and fall in signal amplitude which typically lasts about 9 milliseconds, or about 3½ percent of the pulsar's approximately 0.253 second pulse period. Note that each successive pulse does not occur at precisely the same phase in the pulse cycle. Instead, its timing varies with some degree of randomness. Neither is each pulse the same height as its predecessor.

Precise regularity emerges only when many pulses are averaged together to produce a *time-averaged pulse profile* such as that shown as the uppermost trace in figure 5 which has been synthesized from 2000 successive pulse cycles.* Astronomers find that the shape of this pulse contour remains amazingly constant, being virtually identical to a time-averaged profile synthesized from data obtained some days, months, or even years later. Also unlike the individual pulses, the timing of this average pulse profile is extremely precise, its leading edge always beginning to rise at its "appointed" time. When astronomers speak of the extreme precision of a pulsar's period, they are referring to the timing of the time-averaged profile, rather than to the timing of the individual pulses.

Time-averaged pulse profiles for a number of pulsars are displayed in figure 6. These most often are dominated by a single peak, but some of the wider profiles contain several peaks or components. The pulse profiles generally span anywhere from 1 to 20 percent of a pulsar's total pulsation period, although in some

---

* Pulsar astronomers have come to refer to the individual pulses from a pulsar as "*subpulses*," and the time-averaged pulse profile they have come to call the "*integrated pulse profile.*" Since this terminology could be confusing to some readers, we will adhere to the terms "pulse" and "time-averaged pulse profile" when referring to these concepts in the book.

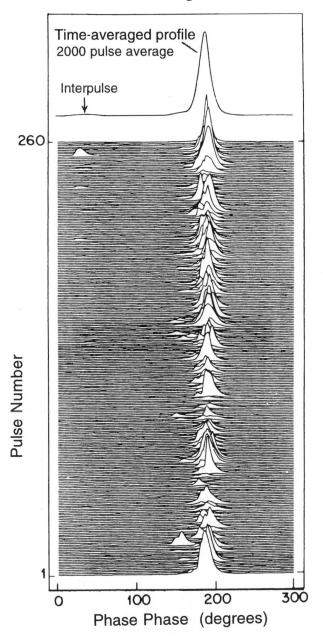

Figure 5. A sequence of 260 pulses received from PSR 0950+08. Their time-averaged pulse profile shown at the top is obtained by adding together 2000 individual pulses. Horizontal axis plots pulse period phase, where one complete cycle is equivalent to a cycle phase of 360° (from Hankins and Cordes, *Astrophysical Journal*, figure 1).

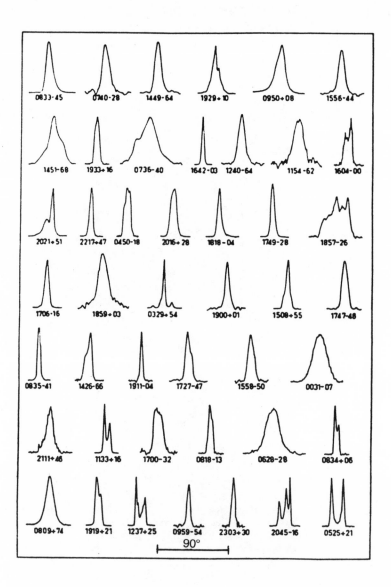

Figure 6. Time-averaged pulse profiles for 45 pulsars. The bar at the bottom indicates the length of a quarter of a pulse cycle (Manchester and Taylor, 1977, figure 1).

cases they stretch over the entire pulse cycle.

At the time when pulsars were first discovered, radio astronomers were not aware of the pulse-to-pulse timing variability. Their radio telescope equipment was set up only to average together many pulses, typically five minutes of collected data. As a result, they were able to study only the time-averaged profile, which happened to exhibit very precise timing. So, it was natural for pulsar theorists to assume that the individual radio pulses being averaged together in the data output were similarly very precisely timed. The neutron star lighthouse model, with its synchrotron beam rotating with clock-like regularity, emerged in the context of this assumption *that the individual pulses were each precisely timed.*

However, within months of the time that Gold had published his neutron star lighthouse model paper, investigators began discovering that there was considerable timing variation from one pulse to the next. This must be attributed mostly to the pulsar and *not* to interstellar scattering of the emitted radio waves during their journey to Earth.* This meant that the basic lighthouse model now had to be radically revised to produce *nonregularly spaced pulses.* This pulse timing irregularity could be produced if the neutron star radiation beam were to flop back and forth as it swept through space. Alternatively, it might occur if the cosmic ray electron beam had a nonuniform substructure, its cosmic rays being concentrated into localized electron cascades, or "sparks," emitted in varying directions through the beam's aperture.

But if the intervals between pulses were to vary in this manner, one would expect that when many pulses were averaged the result would produce a profile whose shape and timing randomly changed from one pulse series average to the next. The finding to the contrary, that the time-averaged pulse profile was instead very constant, indicated that the lighthouse model had to be further revised. Thus as this lighthouse beam swept around, its cosmic ray electron sparks would have to execute their back and forth flickering so that, when observed over many cycles, the sequence of pulses would "paint in"

---

* In the course of their long journey, pulsar signal radio waves can become scattered away from their straight-line trajectory to Earth by intervening clouds of interstellar electrons, an effect that is most pronounced at very low radio frequencies. This can cause the pulsar signal to brighten and fade, much like the twinkling of a star. However, most pulsar observations are conducted at higher frequencies where this scattering variability is minimized. At these higher frequencies the majority of the pulse-to-pulse variability originates from the pulsar itself.

a time-averaged profile that was precisely timed and had a highly ordered shape. For example, the neutron star's sparks might be imagined to pass through a kind of magnetic field "mask" that rotated together with the electron beam. This mask would have an angular width and contour similar to that of the resulting time-averaged pulse profile and would need to influence the sparks so that, as they moved back and forth, the resulting sum total of their "brush strokes" would sketch out the mask's contour. As a result, when the series of synchrotron radiation pulses were added up, they would produce an unvarying time-averaged pulse profile that matched the shape of this mask. But pulsar theorists, then, would need to explain why this postulated magnetic field mask remained so invariant all the while that the neutron star and its cosmic ray beam were spinning so rapidly and sparking in various directions. Commonsense tells us that the powerful cosmic ray beam should instead "blow" the imposed mask much like a wind blowing a flame, and consequently should produce a highly erratic time-averaged pulse profile.

In summary, the lighthouse model offers a very disappointing explanation for even the most basic of pulsar signal characteristics. Its shortcomings are even further compounded when one considers the various other types of ordering that characterizes pulsar signals, some of which are summarized in Appendix B. One example is the phenomenon of pulse *drifting*. In certain pulsars, each succeeding pulse is observed to arrive slightly earlier than its preceding pulse, giving the appearance that the pulses are marching backward at a very regular rate and scanning across the contour of their resulting time-averaged pulse profile. To explain this kind of behavior, yet another level of complexity would need to be added to the lighthouse model. Its rotating cosmic ray beam now could no longer spark erratically in differing directions, but rather would have to produce sparks that swept across its co-rotating magnetic field mask in a highly regular fashion. Moreover, based on observations of certain other pulsars, this pulse drifting model would have to be further revised to abruptly switch from one drift rate to another, and then to another, as if its drifting were being controlled by rudimentary rules of logic. Indeed, *the complexity of pulsar signal ordering far surpasses that of any other known astronomical phenomenon.* Even when the lighthouse model is made absurdly complex, it still falls short of satisfactorily explaining pulsar behavior, a shortcoming that today is widely recognized among pulsar theorists.

ETI Beacons?

Even after the astronomical community had settled on the lighthouse model, some astronomers still entertained the possibility that at least some pulsars might be ETI beacons. Such speculation surfaced in 1974 with the discovery of PSR 1953+29, a pulsar with a very constant pulsation rate. SETI pioneer and pulsar astronomer Frank Drake was one who suggested that this pulsar might have an ETI origin. Dr. Drake is known among other things for having initiated Project OZMA and for having developed an equation for estimating the high probability of intelligent civilizations existing elsewhere in the Galaxy. Regarding this pulsar, he commented:

> All the other pulsars are spinning down, slowing up if you will. Not this one. We can detect no spin-down in this pulsar, making it clearly a very different beast. One other thing it can be is an intelligent civilization attempting to communicate with other worlds, because everybody has said that's how you'd mark yourself. You do something that can't be done in nature. You make the pulse rate of a nearby pulsar exactly right, not deviating in the least year after year.[7]

Observation made over the following years showed that this pulsar's period, in fact, was slowing down, but at a rate thousands of times slower than is typical of most pulsars. It was not by any means unique in this respect since astronomers have subsequently found over a dozen other pulsars that are slowing down at an even slower rate. Pulsar theorists once again came to the rescue of the lighthouse model and added special case assumptions which they believed could account for such an unusually slow loss of rotational speed. But maybe astrophysicists should not be so quick to dismiss the ETI interpretation. If extraterrestrial civilizations are attempting to communicate with us and are distinguishing their transmissions by doing "something that can't be done in nature," then pulsar signals certainly are the closest thing known to fit this criterion.

The chapters that follow present evidence that pulsars are nonrandomly placed in the sky, with particularly distinctive beacons being situated at key Galactic locations that are meaningful reference points from the standpoint of interstellar communication. Of course, these seemingly intelligent sky location placements could be dismissed as just a freak occurrence, albeit a very rare one. Others may instead regard them as evidence of an underlying intelligence operating in nature. Here, we will explore the alternate theory that pulsars are artificial beacons created by advanced ETI civilizations.

But if pulsars have been engineered by intelligent beings, the manner in which they produce their signals must somehow be explained. It is doubtful that their signals originate from space station communicators of the kind portrayed in figure 1. Although such large-scale synchrotron beacons could be designed to produce pulsar-like transmissions, observation suggests that pulsar signals originate from near the surfaces of *star-sized bodies*.

The determination that pulsars are quite massive comes from observations made of pulsars that are orbited by a companion star or planet. In such *binary* pulsars, the gravitational pull of the circling companion causes the pulsar to describe a small orbit in space, thereby inducing a sinusoidal variation in its pulsation period. By analyzing these cyclical variations and taking into account observations of the pulsar's optically visible companion star, astronomers have become convinced that binary pulsars are indeed relatively large celestial bodies having masses comparable to that of our Sun. If we assume that the hundreds of solitary pulsars that fill the sky are not much different from these binaries, we are left to conclude that all pulsar signals similarly arise from objects of rather large mass.

In such a case, does this mean that we must rule out the notion that pulsars may be ETI communication beacons? The answer is no. For example, we might imagine a scientifically advanced civilization seeking out a hot stellar core and making use of its outgoing cosmic ray electron wind for communication purposes. In other words, the electron accelerator component shown in figure 1 would be replaced with a naturally existing stellar cosmic ray source. By using advanced technology of the sort described in chapter 8, magnetic fields might be artificially generated near the star's surface that would, in turn, decelerate the star's cosmic ray electrons and cause them to produce one or more beams of synchrotron radiation (see figure 7). By modulating these fields, synchrotron pulses could be produced similar to those coming from pulsars. As in the particle beam communicator, these beams would be stationary and would be accurately targeted on remote locations. Depending on their degree of divergence, the beam diameters at their remote destinations might vary from the size of a typical solar system (100 times the diameter of the Earth's orbit) to about 100 light years capable of encompassing many star systems.

These communication beacon cosmic ray sources need not be neutron stars; they could instead be white dwarf stars. It is known that such hot stellar cores, which are a common late stage in the

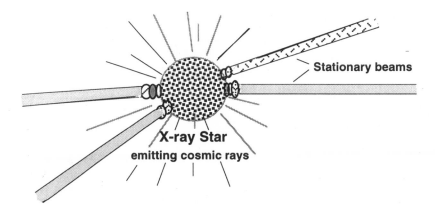

Figure 7. A stationary beam pulsar beacon. Fields engineered near the surface of a cosmic-ray-emitting star project radio synchrotron beams to targeted locations. See chapter 7 for further details.

evolution of a star, typically radiate copious quantities of cosmic ray electrons. They are much larger in diameter than neutron stars (~ 20,000 kilometers, rather than 1 to 20 kilometers) and are about a million times less dense, their interiors consisting of closely packed atoms rather than of closely packed neutrons. As mentioned earlier, when pulsars were first discovered, astrophysicists theorized that their emissions might be produced by white dwarfs that were either rapidly rotating or radially pulsating. But, when short period pulsars such as the Crab and Vela pulsar were discovered, the white dwarf models had to be abandoned since, due to their relatively large size, they could neither rotate or radially oscillate rapidly enough to explain such rapid pulsations. As a result, pulsar astronomers adopted the neutron star model as the only feasible alternative. However, if pulsar signals are of ETI origin, produced by artificially modulated magnetic fields, rather than by natural mechanical movement of the star itself, *a white dwarf would be entirely satisfactory as a cosmic ray source*. The previous mechanical limitations would no longer apply. More will be said about this ETI beam model in chapter 7.

Let us next examine what other characteristics, besides the precise timing of the time-averaged pulse profile, might lead us to conclude that pulsars are communication beacons operated by intelligent beings.

Chapter 2

A Galactic Message

The One-Radian Arrow

Scientists of a communicating Galactic civilization must deal with the problem that their message must surmount an inherent language barrier. They might solve this by framing their message in terms of universal symbols that would be understandable to any advanced civilization. Easily recognizable mathematical or geometric relationships, laws of nature, or major astronomical points of interest might serve as common reference points where a meaningful conversation might begin.

One key location in our own Galaxy that would be an obvious candidate as a reference point is the Galactic center, the fulcrum mass around which the stars of the Milky Way orbit. All civilizations in our Galaxy would perceive this unique site as a central location. NASA scientists referenced this Galactic center location in the space plaque message that was sent out in 1972 onboard the Pioneer 10 spacecraft. It was hoped that an alien civilization capable of spaceflight might one day come upon Pioneer 10 after the craft had journeyed far outside the solar system and discover the message etched on the gold-plated aluminum plaque affixed to its side (figure 8). The long horizontal line extending to the right of the "starburst" diagram on this plaque indicates the solar system's relative distance from the Galactic center, while the other binary coded lines radiating in radial fashion indicate the directions, relative distances, and pulsation periods of fourteen prominent pulsars. By means of these celestial markers it is hoped that an alien civilization might triangulate the spacecraft's point of origin and thereby locate our planet. As will be seen shortly, the pulsars which this diagram innocently uses as reference points may be part of a network of ETI navigation beacons that may themselves be transmitting a message to us.

To receive the Pioneer 10 message, the recipient civilization

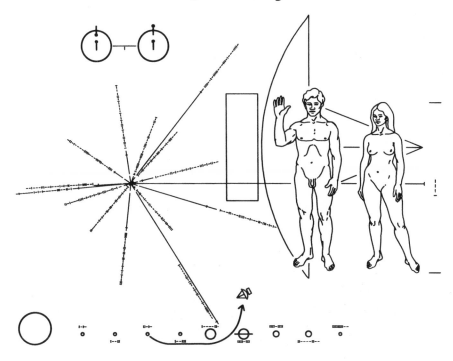

Figure 8. The Pioneer 10 space plaque. The central star-like diagram points out in relation to the Earth the locations and directions of the Galactic center and 14 pulsars.

would actually have to intercept the spacecraft and recognize that its plaque carried a message. However, suppose that a civilization were to attempt to communicate by beaming flashing radio signals through interstellar space. How might beings communicating in this way use the Galactic center reference so that their signal is not mistaken for a natural radio source. One method might be to carefully choose the direction in which they beamed their signal so that the recipient civilization would see it coming from a location that was uniquely positioned relative to the Galactic center, a location that had a particular geometrical meaning easily recognizable to the recipient.

In fact, a careful study reveals that pulsars are nonrandomly distributed in the plane of the sky in such a way that they point out a key location relative to the Galactic center. Consider figure 9 which plots the sky locations of a set of 330 pulsars on a standard galactic coordinate map. The map's coordinate lines measure galactic longitude (ℓ) and latitude (b) much like the longitude and latitude

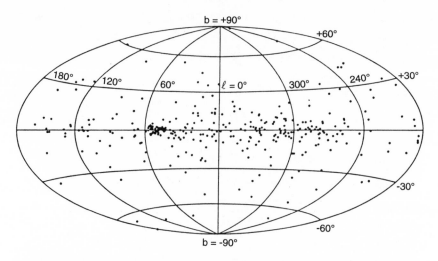

Figure 9. An equal-area projection in galactic coordinates showing the distribution of 330 pulsars (Manchester and Taylor, *Astronomical Journal*, figure 1). The Galactic center is situated at the map's center. The anticenter ($\ell = 180°$, b = 0°) lies at the map's left and right extremities.

lines on a world map.* Our Galaxy's spiral arm disk would stretch out along the map's equator with the Galactic nucleus being located at the map's center. We can get an idea of how the Milky Way's edge-on spiral arm disk and central bulge would appear on such a map by referring to figure 10 which presents a similar mapping of the distribution of the Galaxy's diffuse infrared emission.

As a whole, the pulsars plotted in figure 9 tend to congregate toward the galactic equator, the midline of the spiral arm disk. However, the highest concentration of pulsars is not found near the galactic nucleus, as one might expect if pulsars were natural stellar objects born out of supernova explosions. Instead, the densest concentration is found offset to the left of the map's center between

---

* Convention places zero degrees longitude very close to the Galactic center and sweeps out a full 360° circle as our line of sight moves northward from there, tracking along the Milky Way's equator — the plane formed by the Galaxy's spiral arm disc. Convention measures galactic latitude as angular deviation above or below this equatorial plane, positive angles being toward the galactic north pole situated in Coma Bernices north of the Virgo constellation and negative angles toward the galactic south pole in Sculptor. Astronomers did not know the precise position of the Galactic center at the time they formulated this coordinate system. Consequently, the Galactic center, which later was found to be located at $\ell = -0.056°$, b = $-0.046°$, deviates slightly from the galactic coordinate origin (0,0).

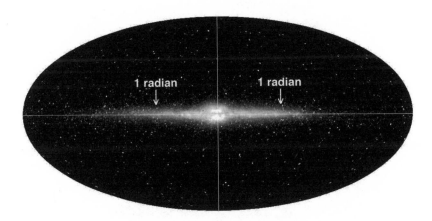

Figure 10. Sky distribution of diffuse infrared emission from the Milky Way at a wavelength of 1 to 3 microns. Data is from NASA's Diffuse Infrared Background Experiment onboard the COBE satellite (courtesy of NASA and COBE Science Working Group).

galactic longitudes 40° and 57°. To a large extent this clumping may be an artifact of the more detailed observation that has been conducted in this part of the sky using the highly sensitive Arecibo telescope. Although many other radio telescopes have been searching the sky for pulsars, the large size of the Arecibo telescope has given it the advantage of being able to detect pulsars that are far more distant and fainter. But, due to its limited degree of maneuverability, surveys made with this telescope have only been able to cover parts of the sky extending from $\ell = 39°$ to $\ell = 66°$, spanning the pulsar clump, and from 170° to 210°, a region lying opposite to the Galactic center. So since Arecibo is better able to find pulsars, a greater number of pulsar detections would be expected in these regions.

It is, however, not so much the existence of greater numbers of pulsars here that is worth noting, but the relative absence of pulsars to the left of this clump. As we proceed past $\ell = 57 \pm 1°$, toward higher galactic longitudes, the number of pulsars drops precipitously. This is a real feature and not an artifact of any sampling bias since the Arecibo telescope has surveyed the sky 9° of longitude past this decline in population and has found few pulsars. Moreover the Green Bank and Jodrell Bank radio telescopes, which have wide sky coverage ability, have supplemented Arecibo in surveying this entire region extending on either side of the clump (see figure 11).

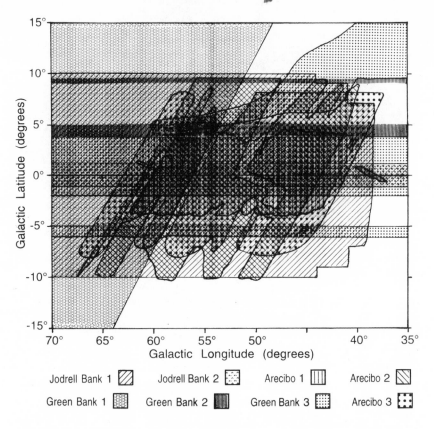

Figure 11. Galactic coordinate map of the region between $\ell = 35°$ and $\ell = 70°$ showing the areas searched in various radio telescope surveys.

The position of this decline in pulsar population relative to the Galactic center is quite striking. For it coincides with the point on the galactic equator that marks an angular deviation *of precisely one radian from the Galactic center.*

What is a radian and why is this particular galactic longitude so special from the standpoint of extraterrestrial communication? The radian is a universal concept that comes from the study of geometry. Let us begin by drawing a circle like that shown in figure 12. If we mark off a length along the circle's circumference that has the same length as the circle's radius, then the angle that subtends this arc, as measured from the center of the circle, is *one radian*. It takes a total of 2π radians to completely circumscribe a circle. Consequently, one radian will equal 360° divided by 2π, or about 57.296 degrees.

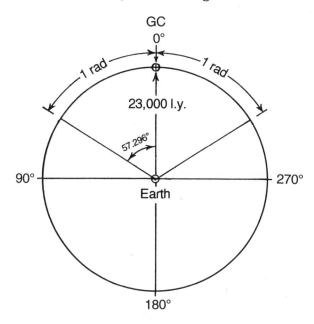

Figure 12. Illustration of the one-radian markers relative to the Galactic center (GC), as viewed from Earth.

Regardless of the size of the circle, this angle will always be the same.

So the radian system uses the circle's own radius as the yardstick for measuring its angles. Although not practical from the standpoint of dividing a circle into a whole number of parts, it does have the advantage that it is based on a simple geometric relation that should be known to any civilization in the Galaxy. As such, it is a prime candidate for use in extraterrestrial communication. We on Earth have chosen to use the *degree* which divides a circle into 360 equal parts, a number that is easily divisible and that approximates the number of days in our solar year. But our scientists and engineers also use the radian for measuring angles, and it would be the radian measure that we would choose if we were to design an ET communication message since we could be assured that it would be known to scientists of other advanced civilizations in the Galaxy who were able to receive our signals.

To see how the radian translates into measurements of galactic longitude, imagine that the circle we have drawn has a radius equal to the distance from our solar system to the center of our Galaxy and whose plane is aligned with the galactic equatorial plane. The Earth would then be positioned at the circle's center, and the Galactic center (GC) would lie at a point on its circumference (see figure 12). Galactic longitude is measured by proceeding counterclockwise around the circle from the Galactic center reference point. Since the true center of the Galaxy is positioned at galactic longitude ℓ = - 0.056°, a one radian angular deviation (57.296°) from this point would lie in the northern celestial hemisphere at galactic longitude ℓ = 57.240°. A second one-radian benchmark would lie in the southern celestial hemisphere at galactic longitude ℓ = 302.652°. The northern one-radian benchmark lies in the vicinity of the Sagitta and Vulpecula constellations and falls very close to the sudden decline in pulsar population. The southern one-radian benchmark lies near the Southern Cross constellation and coincides with the edge of a smaller population decline that will be discussed later.

Implicit in the one radian concept is the notion that the one-radian circumferential arc has a length equal to the radius of the circle. In the context of the galactic coordinate system, the one radian bench-mark would signify an arc length equal to our solar system's distance from the Galactic center. Since the pulsar clump cut off marks the distal end of this one-radian arc, this metaphor would symbolize a 23,000 light-year radial distance that vectors out from the Galactic center and terminates at the Earth.

One Radian Geometrical Rule

The arc length from the Galactic center to the Galactic one-radian benchmark equals the distance from the Galactic center to the Earth.

By pointing out these one-radian locations, the fabricators of this pulsar network, not only would be conveying to us that their signals are of intelligent origin — that they come from beings who have knowledge of circular geometry, but also that their senders know the direction of the Galactic center *as viewed from our solar neighborhood.*

As many as 46 stars similar to our Sun reside within 53 light years of us. If intelligent beings on another star system located some 50 light years from us were to view the heavens, they would see this pulsar clump cut-off displaced in galactic longitude less than a tenth of a degree from the longitude position that we see it in. But, in the case of civilizations viewing the heavens from an entirely different

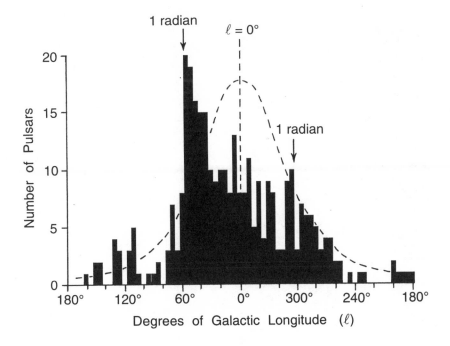

Figure 13. The number of pulsars lying within 5° of the galactic equator plotted as a function of galactic longitude. The left and right arrows indicate longitudes lying one-radian from the Galactic center. The dashed line indicates the profile that would be expected if pulsars were distributed in the Galaxy the same way as supernova remnants.

vantage point on the Galaxy's periphery, say from a location 2000 light years from the Sun, the one-radian direction for them would transect across an entirely different section of the galactic plane. Consequently, the pulsar beacons that might mark the one-radian longitude direction from the vantage point of the solar neighborhood would not mark the one-radian longitude direction as seen by them. Consequently, marking this key one-radian location with a network of beacons would have meaning *only from our particular Galactic locale with its particular perspective for viewing the Galactic center direction.*

We can get a clearer view of this cut-off by displaying our pulsar data in bar graph form, as shown in figure 13. [1] The horizontal axis plots galactic longitude and lays out the Galaxy's 360° circumference in a series of 72 five-degree-wide longitude increments.

Figure 14. The 1000 foot diameter radio telescope at Arecibo, Puerto Rico. The Arecibo Observatory is part of the National Astronomy and Ionosphere Center which is operated by Cornell University under a cooperative agreement with the National Science Foundation (photo courtesy of David Parker, 1997/Science Photo Library).

The vertical axis plots for each longitude increment the number of pulsars lying within five degrees of the galactic equator. The 5° longitude increments have been chosen to begin from $\ell = 357.3°$, rather than $\ell = 0°$ in order to clearly portray the sharp decline after $\ell = 57 \pm 1°$. Within its $\pm 5°$ latitude slice, the map charts a total of 329 pulsars, or about 47 percent of a total sample of 706 pulsars.[*2]

A 2½ fold drop off in pulsar population is evident past the galactic one radian point, $\ell = 57.24°$. As mentioned earlier, this feature is real. It is not attributable to observational selection since it occurs well within the coverage of Arecibo telescope surveys; see figure

---

[*] Most of these detections were made in pulsar surveys that observed at a radio frequency of 400 MHz, although a portion also were detected in 1400 to 1500 MHz surveys. The plotted data set includes the high frequency 1992 Parkes survey which extends from $-90° \le \ell \le 20°$ and $|b| \le 4°$ and the 1992 Jodrell Bank survey which extends from $-5° \le \ell \le 110°$ and $|b| \le 1°$. These are more sensitive than the 400 MHz surveys but the latter covers only one fifth of the latitude range of our data set.

11.* The sudden drop off from a high pulsar population persists even when we plot just the brightest and, hence most easily detectable pulsars. It also persists if we expand our latitude coordinate range to include pulsars lying within ±10° of the galactic equator. Also equally interesting, in proceeding towards increasing galactic longitudes, from ℓ = 42.24° to ℓ = 57.24°, pulsar population progressively rises. This gradual increase cannot be attributed to observational bias since it occurs within the region uniformly surveyed with the Arecibo telescope.

It is difficult to conceive of a natural phenomenon that would reasonably explain a rise and cut-off at this particular galactic longitude region. It cannot be attributed to an enhanced concentration of pulsars distributed along one of the Milky Way's spiral arm since there is no arm aligned along the one-radian direction. The spiral arms instead cut across at an angle to this direction. The sudden drop off also cannot be attributed to the molecular gas ring that circumscribes the Galactic nucleus at a distance of about 14,000 light years. The line-of-sight optical depth of this ring reaches a maximum around ℓ = 30° to 40° and gradually decreases to a minimum value by ℓ = 52°. Consequently, if pulsars were born from stars that may have formed in this ring, their populations should instead have decreased well before the one-radian cut off.

The lighthouse model, which interprets pulsars as spinning neutron stars formed naturally in supernova explosions, predicts that pulsars should be distributed in the Galaxy in much the same way as supernova remnants, as portrayed by the dashed line shown in figure 13.[3] These remnants are scattered throughout the galactic disk and increase in concentration toward the Galactic center conforming to the distribution of the relatively massive, so called "population I" type stars which are believed to be the progenitors of supernovae. However, the supernova remnant distribution profile shows no comparable drop off at the one-radian longitude. The decline away from the Galactic center is more gradual, the downward slope being

---

* For example, the region between galactic longitudes 47.24° and 57.24°, which yield the two highest pulsar counts in the longitude bar chart, has been entirely searched in Arecibo telescope surveys. Also 95% of the adjacent region from 42.24° to 47.24° has been searched in Arecibo surveys, and this has turned up the third highest number of pulsars. However, 95% of the region from 57.24° to 62.24° has also been searched in Arecibo surveys, yet this region which lies beyond the one radian point yields an abnormally low number of pulsars. Besides the Arecibo surveys, there have been five other telescope surveys that have also sought pulsars in this region. So this region has been well searched.

On the other hand, this singular arrangement can be accounted for if pulsars are actually a collectively coordinated network of ETI communicators. To alert our astronomers to the artificial nature of their signals, a number of beacons may have been sited at these sky locations in such a way as to designate from our particular perspective a one-radian arc deviation from the Galactic center.

If pulsars are artificial beacons, this could explain the lack of pulsars in the central part of the Galaxy. This perplexing lack of pulsars within 8,000 light years of the Galactic center (i.e., within $\ell = \pm 20°$) has been carefully studied and documented.[4] As of the time of writing, no pulsar has been found closer than 1700 light years to the Galactic center. Some of the observed deficit may arise because the background radio emission near the galactic nucleus is much higher than other parts of the galaxy and its interference makes it more difficult to detect individual pulsar signals. However, even when this effect is taken into account, an unaccounted for deficit still remains.

Solar systems located in the immediate vicinity of the Galactic core would be expected to be relatively unpopulated since conditions there would be particularly hazardous to life. As mentioned earlier, the center of our Galaxy episodically sends out intense volleys of high energy cosmic rays accompanied by X-ray and gamma ray radiation. Even at a distance of 300 light years from the center, such volleys would be almost 600 times stronger than they would be at our more distant spiral arm location. So, planets that might otherwise be able to support life would be subject to greater hazards in this more hostile part of the Galaxy and would hence be less likely to evolve higher life forms.

Numerous questions come to mind. Are these beacons tightly focused just on our solar system, or can they also be seen by civilizations that might reside in neighboring solar systems? Note that if pulsars are not spinning neutron stars, as the conventional lighthouse model proposes, and if they instead emit fixed beams, as was suggested in the last chapter, then the signals we are receiving from a given pulsar might not be detected by civilizations residing sufficiently far off to one side of the beam. In that case other beams would have to be targeted to communicate with those destinations. If so, has this network of Galactic civilizations gone to similar efforts to target other sectors of the Galaxy as well?

The sheer magnitude of such an interstellar communication

project causes one to pause. Is it possible that Galactic civilizations would set up so many beacons and maintain them over such a long period just to communicate with our particular region? Perhaps there might be some auxiliary purpose for their deployment such as their use as reference points for navigating spacecraft throughout the Galaxy. Surely, in the face of such a radical proposal, many of us are inclined to be skeptical and would demand further proof than just the existence of this pulsar cut-off feature. Indeed, we have barely scratched the surface; we will discover even more unusual "coincidences" in the chapters that follow.

Superluminal Space Travel

If pulsars are ETI beacons that have been fabricated by technically advanced Galactic civilizations, their existence would have some very profound implications. Not only would it indicate that intelligent life exists elsewhere in the Galaxy, but also that it exists in numerous parts of the Galaxy. To carefully craft a distribution of pulsars that stretches out over a distance of more than 100,000 light years, civilizations in these diverse locations would have to be in close cooperation over a comparable duration of light-travel time. Not only does this require a functioning Galactic communication network, a kind of "Galactic internet," it also requires a very long-term collective commitment by these civilizations.

The task of orchestrating an organized pulsar array covering such vast distances would only be possible if these civilizations either had developed the means for faster-than-light space travel or the means of communicating among themselves at speeds far greater than the speed of light. Physicist Miguel Alcubierre has now shown that superluminal space travel is in principle physically possible, that it does not necessarily violate the theory of general relativity which academic physicists still revere. In his 1994, scientific journal paper entitled "The warp drive: Hyperfast travel within general relativity," he suggests that if a spacecraft were to be able to alter space-time in its vicinity so as to compress space-time at its bow (similar to a large positive mass) and dilate space-time at its stern (similar to a large negative mass), the effect could propel the craft through space-time at superluminal speeds.[5] Commenting on this paper, physicist Hal Puthoff has stated:

> In SETI (Search for Extraterrestrial Intelligence) conventional wisdom has it that the probability of direct contact by interstellar

travel is vanishingly small due to the enormous distance involved, coupled with the velocity-of-light limitation. Alcubierre's recent "warp drive" analysis within the context of general relativistic dynamics, however, indicates the naïveté of this assumption. We show here that Alcubierre's result is a particular case of a broad, general approach that might loosely be called "metric engineering," the results of which provide yet further support for the concept that reduced-time interstellar travel, either by advanced extraterrestrial civilizations at present or ourselves in the future, is not, as naïve consideration might hold, fundamentally constrained by physical principles.[6]

Extensive research into gravity control engineering, had been going on as far back as the early twentieth century with the electrogravitics work of physicist and inventor T. Townsend Brown. He demonstrated that when a high-voltage charge is applied, a capacitor will experience a gravitational thrust in the direction of its positive pole.[7-9] The aerospace industry began an intensive study of this phenomenon back in the mid 50's, and there is an indication that the B2 bomber incorporates an electrogravitic drive based on ideas described in Brown's patents.[10,11] The new physics methodology of *subquantum kinetics*, among other things, offers a theoretical framework that predicts electrogravitic coupling, although it does not construe the effect in terms of space-time warping. Rather, it describes this force as arising through the action of a *gravity potential gradient*.[12,13] So, subquantum kinetics predicts that future superluminal craft may employ electrogravitic "*gradient drive*," rather than "warp drive." Regardless of how the gravity drive concept is construed, further progress in gravity engineering could one day lead us to the reality of superluminal travel.

Spaceflight Navigation

If extraterrestrial civilizations have developed superluminal spaceflight, they would need a means for charting their course through the Galaxy. One might consider, then, whether the primary function of the pulsar network is for use in space navigation. The pulsar network might function something like our own Global Positioning System. The GPS is an array of radio signal transmitting satellites that have been placed in geosynchronous orbit to ensure that they remain stationary above the Earth's surface. By triangulating their signals, cars, ships, aircraft, and hikers are able to accurately locate their position on the Earth's surface.

NASA scientists used the pulsar network for navigation purposes when they sent out their ET communication message on board the Pioneer 10 spacecraft. As described earlier, an alien civilization coming across Pioneer 10 and its space plaque could locate the craft's Earth-based point of origin by identifying the particular pulsars designated on the plaque and using them to triangulate the Sun's location. In a similar fashion, by locking onto the signals of several pulsars, a spaceship could accurately locate its *instantaneous position* in the Galaxy. Equally importantly, the ship would also be able to determine its *instantaneous velocity* by taking note of Doppler compression or expansion of the pulsar signals. Just as the pitch of a horn is Doppler shifted, increased or decreased depending upon the relative velocity of the listener, similarly, the pulsation rate of a pulsar signal would be increased or decreased from its Galactic rest frame pulsation rate depending upon the spacecraft's relative velocity.

For example, let us suppose that we are onboard a spaceship bound for a star near the Crab Nebula, Taurus constellation. Suppose that before we start out we target the Crab Nebula pulsar with our onboard radio telescope and, observing it at a radio frequency of 606 megahertz, we find it to have a pulsation cycle period of 33.403 milliseconds. Its time-averaged pulse profile would look as shown in figure 15-a.* Now suppose that our spacecraft accelerates toward the Crab Nebula and reaches a velocity of 33 percent of light speed (0.33c). Upon reobserving this navigation beacon, we would find that the Crab pulsar now is pulsing 41% faster with a period of 23.709 milliseconds and would appear as shown in figure 15-b. Also the Doppler shift effect resulting from our velocity toward the pulsar would produce an apparent 41% increase in the pulsar's radio wave frequencies in direct proportion to the shortening of the pulsar's period. The radio frequencies that had been forming the pulsar's 606 megahertz pulse profile when we were at rest would now be observed by us to be blue shifted up to 854 megahertz. So by observing both the location and pulse rate of pulsars, it should be possible to judge our direction and speed of travel.

However, to accurately judge our speed relative to the Galactic rest frame, we would need to make a time correction. That is, since

---

* It would probably be more realistic to assume that the space travelers observed the pulsar at a higher frequency in the gigahertz range since the radio telescope dish for observing at this radio frequency would be rather bulky to take along on their trip. But, this example is suitable for the purpose of illustration.

Figure 15. Pulse periods and pulse profiles for the Crab Nebula pulsar as seen from two different reference frames: a) the solar reference frame (v = 0) observed at a frequency of 606 MHz, and b) the in-flight reference frame (v = 0.33c) observed at a frequency of 845 MHz (adapted from Moffet and Hankins, *The Astrophysical Journal*, figure 2).

we are traveling at 33% of the speed of light, our onboard atomic clocks would be ticking about 6 percent slower due to the relativistic clock retardation effect. However, since we would not know our exact velocity, we would not know how much our clocks had slowed or how much of a correction to make to our pulse period observations. Moreover since we would not be able to accurately interpret the pulsar periods, we would, in turn, not be able to accurately determine our velocity. Fortunately, there would be a way out of this bind. The pulsar beacons have been designed so that their periods gradually increase over time. By knowing the normal slow down rate for a given pulsar in the galaxy rest frame and by reobserving that pulsar's slow down rate from our spaceship, we can accurately determine the degree to which our clocks have retarded. For example, when our spaceship was initially at rest, we would have found that the Crab pulsar's period was increasing at the rate of about 1.088 millionths of a pulse period per day. While traveling at 0.33c, this period change would now seem to us to take place

5.605% slower at the rate of about 1.030 millionths of a pulse period per day. Knowing this, we could now correct the pulsar period that we had observed, shortening it by 5.605% from 23.709 milliseconds to 22.380 milliseconds. We could then realize that we are actually traveling at 0.33c in the galactic reference frame, 12 percent faster than what we thought our speed was before we made this correction.*

The pulsar network, then, *is ideal for space navigation*. Being easily distinguished from one another, pulsars provide a means whereby a spacecraft may accurately determine its location through triangulation. They also allow accurate determination of velocity from the Doppler shift of the pulsar periods and of clock retardation from the change in the pulsar period derivatives. Moreover their broad spectrum makes these beacons ideally suited for high-speed interstellar flight. It allows their signals to be detected by narrow band radio receivers on board spacecraft traveling at almost any speed, regardless of the degree of Doppler frequency shifting.

Superluminal Communication

If one is not prepared to accept the possibility that civilizations might cross such vast stretches of interstellar space at superluminal speeds, one might still consider the possibility that they could share information among themselves at superluminal speeds. Is such communication possible? Maybe it is. In 1991, Thomas Ishii and George Giakos reported that they had transmitted microwaves at faster than light speeds.[14,15] Shortly afterward in 1992, Enders and Nimtz, physicists at the University of Cologne in Germany, described transmitting microwaves through an undersized waveguide at superluminal velocity.[16] This work became more widely known after 1995 when this group succeeded in transmitting Mozart's 40th symphony through an undersized 11 centimeter long waveguide at a speed 4.7 times faster than that of light.[17] Other physicists have been exploring the possibility of using quantum-entangled photon pairs as

---

* Measuring just the change in pulsar period will not be sufficient to allow a space traveler to accurately determine his velocity since his measurement of the pulsar period is not only affected by his velocity but by the retardation of his clock as well. He could unambiguously determine his velocity from the pulsar period either by accurately knowing his direction of travel relative to the pulsar or by using an independent method for determining his clock retardation, such as by measuring the pulsar period derivative.

Figure 16. The electrogravitic communication transmitter (left) and receiver (right) developed by T. Townsend Brown.

a way of sending information virtually instantaneously from one point in space to another.

Earlier researchers had explored a far less sophisticated technique that could transmit messages over great distances by means of longitudinal wave shock fronts. Physicist T. Townsend Brown, for example, had developed a communication device that generated its signals by repeatedly charging a capacitor to a high-voltage and abruptly discharging it through a spark gap. The resulting energy shock fronts so produced were received by an electrified capacitor bridge that registered these waves as voltage transients read by means of a Brush chart recorder (see figure 16). His original bridge used titanium oxide capacitors. An investigator from the Office of Naval Research who witnessed a test of this device in 1952 reported that signals were successfully transmitted to a receiver located in an adjoining room within an electrically grounded metal shield.[18]

In a September 1953 patent disclosure, Brown described another version of this communication device that used massive electrically conductive spheres for both the transmitter and receiver antennae and which was designed to convey audio frequency signals.[19] An article printed in *Inter Avia* magazine in 1956 indicated that Brown suspected that the waves being transmitted were not limited by the speed of light, although at the time he had no definitive proof of this.[20] Since he had determined that his capacitor bridge was able to detect gravitational disturbances, he concluded that the signals he was conveying must be gravitic, rather than electromagnetic. He reasoned that the waves were the gravitational homologues of light waves, which, for lack of a better word, he called "quasi-light." His gravitic hypothesis found further support in his discovery that even better reception was obtained if he replaced the two titanium oxide capacitors in his bridge circuit with ceramic capacitors that had both a high mass density and high dielectric constant.

Brown's transmitter bore a strong resemblance to the monopolar radio frequency generators built by scientist and inventor Nikola Tesla in the late nineteenth and early twentieth centuries. These similarly produced sawtooth pulses and were radiated from a high-voltage antenna terminating in a metal sphere. Also, like Tesla's waves, Brown's pulses penetrated through Faraday cage shields. Like Tesla before him, Brown theorized that the waves he was producing were non-Hertzian. In other words, conventional Hertzian electromagnetic waves are produced when electrical charges oscillate from side to side, for example along an antenna dipole, and as a result their waves consist of forces that are oriented transverse to the direction of wave travel. Brown's waves, on the other hand, were produced by an oscillatory rise and fall of electrical charge on a monopole antenna, and so consisted of field gradients that were oriented primarily *longitudinally* to the direction of wave travel. Whereas Hertzian waves travel at the speed of light in free space (their round-trip average velocity), longitudinal waves need not be similarly limited.[21]

In summary, existing experimental evidence suggests that faster-than-light communication may be possible. Assuming that communicators can be built to transmit superluminal signals over interstellar distances, message time lags between civilizations would be minimal, thereby making possible an integrated Galactic internet. Could the Hertzian electromagnetic emissions from pulsars contain a non-Hertzian superluminal component, as yet unidentified, that permits such rapid communication? Or would such communications be transmitted from entirely different beacon arrays?

Chapter 3

One-Radian Marker Beacons

The Millisecond Pulsar

A close study of the galactic coordinate map shown in figure 17, reveals that there is one pulsar that comes quite close to the Galaxy's northern one-radian point, which marks an angle of one radian from the center of the Galaxy. This pulsar, designated as PSR 1937+21, deviates from this key equatorial location by just 0.4 degrees of arc! Also its longitude coordinate deviates by just 0.27 degrees from the longitude meridian passing through this one-radian point. The pulsar's galactic coordinates ·are (ℓ = 57.51°, b = - 0.29°), as compared with (ℓ = 57.24°, b = 0°) for the northern one-radian point. As we saw in the last chapter, an enhanced concentration of pulsars, or arrow-like clump, is located in this region and appears to intentionally indicate this northern one-radian longitude, thereby implying that pulsars may be of ETI origin. If the ETI hypothesis is correct, we might imagine that the extraterrestrial civilizations that created them would want to further mark this one-radian longitude by ensuring that the one pulsar that is placed closest to this point is unique.

In fact, pulsar PSR 1937+21 ranks as one of the most attention grabbing of all known pulsars. It happens to be *the fastest pulsar in the sky*. It flashes about 642 times per second, each of its cycles spanning just 1.5578064688197941 thousandths of a second.[1,2] If its flashes could be heard, they would sound a note of E above high C. In addition, to pulsing very rapidly, its pulsation period is unusually constant, increasing by just 3.3 trillionths of a second each year. With its timing characteristics presently being known to 17 significant figures, this beacon now *surpasses the best atomic clocks in its precision*. It is indeed interesting to find that it marks the very tip of the pulsar clump arrow.

Most pulsars have much slower pulse periods, ranging from tenths of a second to a few seconds. However, there are a small fraction that pulse very rapidly, so rapidly that they stretch the

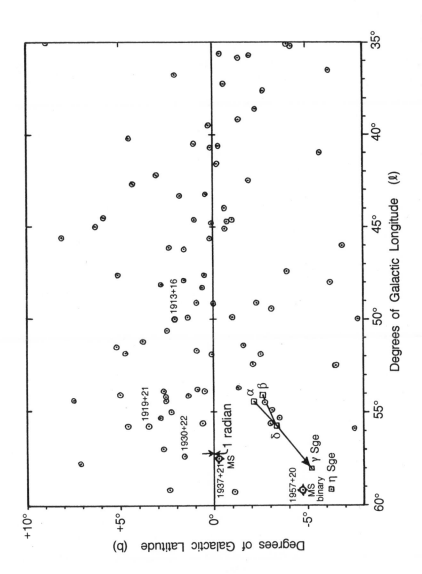

Figure 17. A close-up view showing the positions of pulsars lying between $\ell = 43°$ and $\ell = 57.5°$. The positions of five stars forming the constellation of Sagitta (The Celestial Arrow) are marked by squares.

spinning neutron star model beyond the limits of credibility. Pulsars such as these having periods shorter than 10 milliseconds (pulse rates greater than 100 times per second) have been termed "millisecond pulsars." At the time of writing, astronomers have discovered a total of about 50, and the number is slowly rising.

Because of its unique status as "chief" of the millisecond pulsars, PSR 1937+21 has been formally named the *Millisecond Pulsar*. Besides being the fastest pulsar, the Millisecond Pulsar is unique in several other ways. At radio frequencies it is the most luminous of all millisecond pulsars. Compared with other pulsars in the millisecond category, it emits 10 to 100 times more energy. At its distance of 11,700 light years, it is the second brightest millisecond pulsar in the sky, surpassed by another that is brighter only because it happens to lie 25 times closer to us. Moreover in step with its radio frequency pulses, it also emits flashes of light that are visible with optical telescopes. Optical flashing is a very rare phenomenon *observed in only two other pulsars*, the Crab and Vela supernova remnant pulsars. Among millisecond pulsars, PSR 1937+21 is the only one emitting optical pulses.

The Millisecond Pulsar is also unique in that it is *one of only two pulsars known to emit giant pulses*, the other being the Crab Nebula pulsar. Giant pulses are rare pulses whose intensity exceeds the average pulse intensity by many fold. In the case of the Millisecond Pulsar, about one radio pulse in ten thousand is more than 20 times more intense than the norm and one pulse in 800,000, coming about once every 20 minutes, exceeds the norm by 100 fold. When emitting a giant pulse of such high intensity, the Millisecond Pulsar becomes the brightest pulsar in the sky, thereby allowing it to be easily detected by recipient civilizations. The distinguishing features of emitting both optical pulses and giant pulses single out this pulsar as an appropriate marker beacon, one that flashes its impetuous warning 642 times per second to get our attention to this key Galactic location at the tip of the pulsar clump arrow.

Another feature that distinguishes the Millisecond Pulsar as a marker beacon is that it hardly moves from its sky location. Due to their characteristic velocities, pulsars move relative to distant background stars as do most nearby stars. Astronomers call this *proper motion*. As of the time of writing, proper motions have been determined for about 94 pulsars, and of these, the Millisecond Pulsar is found to have the lowest proper motion. Its position changes by only 0.7 ± 3.0 seconds of arc per millennium.[3]

So, in summary, several features together make the Millisecond Pulsar a likely candidate as a marker beacon. It is the fastest pulsing pulsar; it emits optically visible pulses that facilitate easy detection; it is the most luminous of all known millisecond pulsars; it regularly produces high intensity pulses called "giant pulses", its time-averaged pulse profile exhibits extreme regularity, and it has a very low proper motion (see Table 1, p. 47).

The odds that any one given pulsar will come within 0.4 degrees of the one-radian benchmark are about 1 in 10,000. Repeating this throw of the dice 1100 times for the 1100 known pulsars, the odds that any pulsar of average brightness ends up residing this close to this benchmark are about 1 in 9. However, the odds that a pulsar that is as unique as the Millisecond Pulsar should end up being the one to hold this honor, and no other out of 1100 pulsars, is far smaller, about one chance in 10 raised to the 4400th power. The odds are overwhelmingly against nature having arranged this placement. If we had to choose between coincidental placement near this key Galactic location and purposeful placement by a Galactic civilization, the odds seem to lean heavily in favor of the ETI alternative.

One might ask that since this pulsar has such a low velocity in the plane of the sky, why does it deviate by 0.4 degrees from the one-radian point, if it was intended to accurately mark this location? A shift in our viewing direction by just 50 light years in a direction away from the Galactic center would cause a parallax change in the position of the Millisecond Pulsar sufficient to place it exactly in coincidence with the Galactic one-radian point. So, this might be an indication that this marker is intended generally for our local solar neighborhood and not just for our solar system in particular. On the other hand, this discrepancy could be due to the limitations involved in sighting the beacon. As is discussed in chapter 7, an extraterrestrial civilization could create pulsar communication beacons by seeking out naturally existing stellar cosmic ray sources and engineering them to produce the observed pulses. If so, the Millisecond Pulsar may have been the only stellar source that could be found that would be seen from our viewing perspective to lie close to the one-radian longitude benchmark.

We cannot help noticing a similarity between the pulsar clump and the ancient constellation of Sagitta which portrays the Celestial Arrow, both of which have their far tip situated near the Galaxy's northern one-radian point. In the case of the constellatory Arrow, the arrow tip is represented by the star Gamma Sagittae (γ Sge) which is located in the sky at (ℓ = 57.966°, b = - 5.207°). Of all visible constellation stars, Gamma Sagittae comes nearest to the Galaxy's northern one-radian benchmark, deviating in longitude by just 0.75°. In fact, there is strong evidence to suggest that the ancient astronomers who outlined the Sagitta constellation knew the location of the Galactic center and purposely marked this one-radian point. Consequently, in terrestrial star lore, Gamma Sagittae stands as the counterpart for the Millisecond Pulsar, both of which designate this key Galactic location.

The Vulpecula pulsar (PSR 1930+22) is also of interest (see figure 18). Being positioned in the Vulpecula constellation at (57.357°, +1.555°), near the "tip" of the "one-radian pulsar grouping," it is the *second* closest pulsar to the northern Galactic one-radian point. It is also the *closest* pulsar to the longitude meridian that passes through this equatorial one-radian point, deviating from this meridian by just 0.12 degrees. Interestingly, the Millisecond Pulsar and the Vulpecula pulsar, the two pulsars that come nearest to the northern Galactic one-radian point, are so positioned that a trajectory line drawn through their locations currently passes within just 0.05 degrees of arc of Gamma Sagittae, the pointer star of the Celestial Arrow.* It is difficult to interpret this close alignment as just a coincidence. If this pulsar indicator is an artificial beacon intentionally placed by a Galactic collective of intercommunicating civilizations, then they would have had to know how the night sky appears from our particular galactic locale, that of the bright stars nearest our solar system, Gamma Sagittae is the only one seen from our general locale to come closest to the Galactic one-radian point, a benchmark whose sky position is determined by our particular viewing direction.

The Sagitta constellation is part of an ancient constellation lore message that uses the language of archetypal metaphor to record the past occurrence of a Galactic core explosion.[4,5] This relates how an intense cosmic ray wind issued from the Galactic center and showered our solar system close to the end of the ice age. As noted in the next chapter, Sagitta symbolizes this cosmic ray volley that journeyed from the Galactic center to the solar system, a distance equal to Sagitta's one-radian arc flight from the Galactic center.

---

* The alignment would have been exact around 1780 B.C., but since then has worsened due to Gamma Sagittae's gradual lateral movement, or "proper motion."

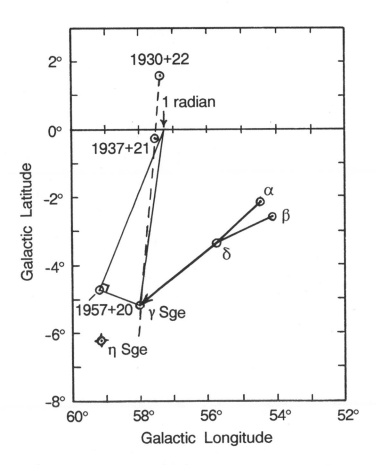

Figure 18. A sky diagram showing the location of the Millisecond Pulsar (PSR 1937+21), Eclipsing Binary Millisecond Pulsar (PSR 1957+20), and the Vulpecula pulsar (PSR 1930+22) relative to the stars that form the constellation of Sagitta, the Celestial Arrow.

The Eclipsing Binary Millisecond Pulsar

PSR 1957+20 is another distinctive millisecond pulsar that happens to be located in this key part of the sky and that in many respects is fully as unique as the Millisecond Pulsar.[4] It is situated 5000 light years from us in the Sagitta constellation. Although not contributing to the one-radian pulsar group, it is positioned nearby at ($\ell = 59.197°$, b = -4.697), just beyond the longitude where pulsar population drops off sharply. This pulsar ranks ninth among all pulsars in constancy, its period increasing by just one half trillionth of a second each year. So, like the Millisecond Pulsar, it excels as a Galactic time standard. Also it is particularly unusual in that it is the *second fastest* pulsator of the pulsar family. Astoundingly, its period of 1.60740168480632 milliseconds exceeds the length of the Millisecond Pulsar's period by just 3.18 percent.

It is indeed very unusual that the two most rapid pulsators in the Galaxy, would not only have periods *so nearly identical*, but also that they would be positioned in the sky *so close together*, within 4.5° of one another, *and so near this galactic one-radian point*. Astronomers who have studied these two millisecond pulsars have made no comment about the proximity of these pulsars to this key geometrical point, probably because they have not seriously considered the ETI connection. Nevertheless the close mutual proximity of these two unusual sources has caught the attention of some. It inspired astronomer Dan Stinebring to jokingly refer to this region as "Pulsar Heaven" because, as he jestingly put it, "that seems to be where the most interesting stars go after they die".[5] In alluding to pulsars as "dead stars," he presumes, as the majority of astronomers, that a pulsar is a spinning neutron star, hence a stellar core remaining after the explosive death of its progenitor star.

PSR 1957+20 differs from the Millisecond Pulsar in that it is a *binary* pulsar, meaning that it is orbited by a companion star. The pulsar's cosmic ray wind continually blows gas off the surface of its orbiting companion causing the two to be enveloped in a small nebula (figure 19). Interestingly, studies of the pulsar's proper motion show that it is moving toward the Galactic center. This relative motion through the interstellar medium causes a wind to blow toward the nebula from the Galactic center direction. As a result, the nebula's upwind, Galactic-center side is compressed into a bow shape and its leeward side is blown back in a cometary fashion.

Astronomers are able to determine the orbital characteristics of a binary pulsar to a high degree of accuracy by observing the cyclical increase and decrease in its period that occurs as the pulsar and its companion star orbit one another. PSR 1957+20, for example, has been found to describe a highly circular orbit having a radius of 26,770 kilometers. Its orbit is so precisely formed that it *deviates from perfect circularity by less than one part per billion*! Three other pulsars are known to have orbits even more circular than this. By comparison, the Earth's orbit around the Sun deviates from perfect circularity by more than one part in 10,000.

Another noteworthy aspect of this binary millisecond pulsar is that

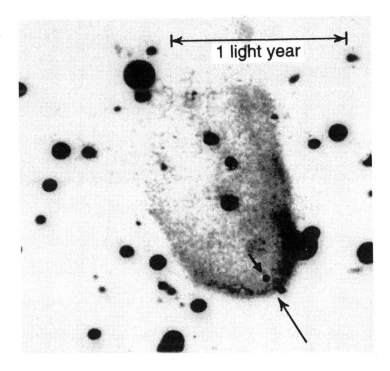

Figure 19. The cometary nebula around the binary millisecond pulsar PSR 1957+20 and its companion star. The position of the companion is indicated by the small downward arrow. The superimposed upward arrow indicates the direction of approach for an interstellar wind blowing from the Galactic center direction (Kulkarni and Hester, *Nature*, figure 3; photo courtesy of S. R. Kulkarni).

its companion star (or planet) periodically passes in front of it, temporarily occluding its signal. About 29 pulsars are presently known to be associated with an orbiting partner star, but of these *only six* have their orbital planes so oriented that the partner periodically blocks the pulsar's signals. PSR 1957+20 happens to be one of these. Every 9.2 hours, when its partner passes between us and the pulsar, the pulsar's signals are eclipsed for about 50 minutes. The eclipsing phenomenon indicates that we lie quite close to the binary pulsar's orbital plane, or in other words that the binary's orbital plane is oriented edge-on relative to us. We are left to wonder whether it is just a stroke of chance that this unique pulsar, the second fastest pulsator in the sky, *happens to trace out an orbit that is aimed in our particular viewing direction*. It is worth considering whether this may be through intelligent design, an indication that this is a message meant for our Galactic locale.

Because it is equally as unique as the Millisecond Pulsar, we will distinguish PSR 1957+20 with the proper name *Eclipsing Binary Millisecond Pulsar,* or "EBM Pulsar" for short. Three other eclipsing binary pulsars are known to lie close the galactic equator, and these too are situated at key locations. Two of these, PSR 1718-19 (ℓ = 4.9°, b = 9.7°) and PSR 1744-24A (ℓ = 3.85°, b = 1.70°), have sky positions within several degrees of the Galactic center. The fourth, PSR 1259-63 (ℓ = 304.22°, b = -0.98°), lies in the Southern Cross constellation, Crucis (The Cross), near the Galaxy's southern one-radian point (see figure 20). The southern and northern eclipsing binary pulsars are separated from one another by 114.98°. Divided in half, this yields 57.49° which is just 0.2° from being exactly equal to one radian! The midpoint of this 115 degree chord falls near the Galactic center at (ℓ = 1.71°, b = -2.84°) not far from the other two eclipsing binary pulsars.

Consideration must be given whether this is all just coincidental, or whether these eclipsing binaries may be part of some Galactic plan to convey to their viewers the concept of one radian, an arc equal to the distance from the Galactic center to the solar environs. Since these one-radian pulsar markers are binaries that have orbital planes aimed specifically in our direction, we are left to consider that this one-radian message may be addressed to us.

This tri-marker placement: 1) at the northern one-radian point, 2) near the Galactic center, and 3) at the southern one-radian point, parallels the tri marker designations found in our own star lore constellations. Sagitta (The Celestial Arrow) designates the northern benchmark, the arrow in Sagittarius' bow and the stinger of Scorpius designate the Galactic center, and the cross of the Crucis constellation marks out the southern benchmark (figure 20). An arc of length one radian, measured from the Galactic center (ℓ = 359.944°, b = -0.046°) southward along the Galactic equator, terminates at longitude 302.65°. This falls just beneath Beta Crucis, the star at the tip of the constellation crossbar that points toward the Galactic center. The Southern Cross eclipsing binary pulsar lies just 1.8° from this point. It may be worth noting that pulsar concentration along the galactic plane drops off sharply just beyond the galactic longitude for this southern one-radian point (see figure 13 and figure A.1 of Appendix A). This sudden decrease in pulsar population is similar to the sharp decline at the northern one-radian point, but not as pronounced.

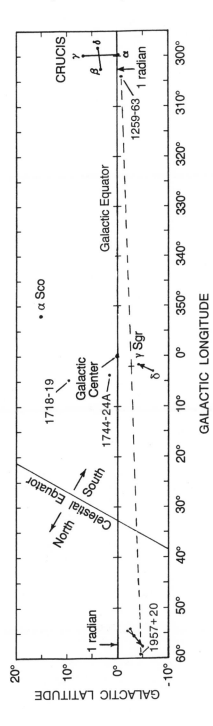

Figure 20. The Galactic center one-radian benchmarks along the Galactic equator compared with the positions of Sagitta and Crucis and with the locations of the four eclipsing binary millisecond pulsars.

Of the two eclipsing binary pulsars that have sky positions near the Galactic center, PSR 1744-24A actually lies physically close to the Galactic core, residing in globular cluster Terzan 5 just 1700 light years from this central location. At the time of this writing, Terzan has the distinction of being the one pulsar that comes physically closest to the Galactic center, although this situation may change as new pulsars are discovered in the Parkes Multibeam survey. For this pulsar to lie so close to the Galactic center and also be one of just six known eclipsing binary pulsars is indeed quite attention grabbing. Interestingly, the Terzan eclipsing binary pulsar has a sky position that lies just 3 degrees away from the point on the galactic equator ($\ell = 6.4°$, b = 0°) where the plane of the ecliptic, the Earth's orbital plane, intersects the galactic plane.

The 1.6 millisecond EBM Pulsar, like its sibling the Millisecond Pulsar, is positioned at a key sky location that calls attention to the one-radian concept in yet another way. Namely, of all pulsars, its sky position comes closest to that of Gamma Sagittae, the constellation star that marks the tip of the one-radian arrow. In fact, this pulsar is so positioned at ($\ell = 59.197°$, b = -4.697°) that its sighting through Gamma Sagittae makes almost an exact right angle with its sighting through the galactic one-radian point (see figure 18). Presently, the angle between these trajectories is 90.04°, or essentially a right angle, to the extent that we know the location of the Galactic equator in this part of the sky. In addition, the pulsar's galactic longitude is almost the same as that of Eta Sagittae, the "target star" toward which the Celestial Arrow is flying, deviating by less than a minute of arc. The seemingly careful positioning of the two fastest millisecond pulsars and the Vulpecula pulsar (PSR 1930+22) relative to the Gamma Sagittae arrow-head star is quite astounding. The possibility presents itself that a network of extraterrestrial civilizations have carefully chosen the positions of these pulsars, knowing the layout of stars in our part of the Galaxy. Alternatively, it may be worth considering that nearby members of a network of communicating civilizations visited our planet long ago and traced out for our ancestors the Sagitta constellation and other asterisms and instructed them to pass down this extraterrestrial star lore through the generations.

Considering that Sagitta symbolizes the cosmic ray wind that issued from the Galactic center and showered our solar system close to the end of the ice age, is it just a coincidence that the EBM Pulsar, the closest pulsar to Sagitta's arrow tip star, has a nebula that looks as if it is being blown back by a wind coming from the Galactic center direction? If the solar system were struck by a cosmic ray wind from the Galactic center, the heliopause plasma sheath that surrounds the solar system would similarly have been pressed back into a cometary shape.

Several distinctive features of the two unique Galactic one-radian point markers, the Millisecond Pulsar and the EBM Pulsar, are summarized in Table 1. The chances are exceedingly small that two so uniquely placed pulsars would randomly develop so many unique features through natural causes.

TABLE 1

Distinctive Features of the One-Radian Point Pulsar Markers

The Millisecond Pulsar

1) Is the fastest pulsator in the sky.

2) Is the most luminous of all millisecond pulsars.

3) Is one of just three pulsars that emits optical pulses.

4) Is one of just two pulsars that emits giant pulses.

5) Is the closest pulsar to the Galaxy's northern one-radian point.

6) Is the most stationary pulsar; has the lowest proper motion of any pulsar.

7) A line extending through PSR 1930+22, the closest pulsar to the one-radian meridian, grazes Gamma Sagittae, the constellation star that comes closest to the northern one radian point.

The Eclipsing Binary Millisecond (EBM) Pulsar

1) Is the second fastest pulsator in the sky.

2) Its period deviates from that of the Millisecond Pulsar by just 3.18%. As a fraction of a circle, this equals 1/5 of a radian.

3) It lies within 4.5 degrees of arc of the Millisecond Pulsar.

4) Is one of just 6 eclipsing binary pulsars, pulsars whose orbital planes happen to be oriented edge-on in our direction.

5) Is the closest pulsar to Gamma Sagittae, the one radian point indicator star.

6) A line drawn from this pulsar through the Galaxy's northern one-radian point makes a right angle with a line drawn from this pulsar through the Gamma Sagittae indicator star.

7) The pulsar is surrounded by a nebula being pushed back by a wind coming from the Galactic center direction.

Chapter 4

The Galactic Imperative

Message in the Stars

Earlier we saw that Sagitta, the Celestial Arrow constellation, closely indicates the Galaxy's northern one-radian point, the point along the galactic equator that deviates one radian of arc from the Galactic center. A close study of constellation lore reveals that it is part of a larger constellation cipher, one that includes the southern constellations of Centaurus, and Crucis as well as the constellations of the zodiac and their astrological lore. As explained in the Author's books *Beyond the Big Bang* and *Earth Under Fire*, these ancient asterisms and their associated lore use the language of metaphor to convey that the Galactic center underwent a major explosion and that cosmic rays and radiation from this outburst began to shower our solar system around 16,000 years ago, bringing about a global climatic disaster.[1,2] By designating the Galaxy's northern one-radian point, this message was able to convey the idea of how the energy released from this Galactic center explosion had traveled radially outward through the Galaxy to ultimately impact the solar system.

Let us briefly summarize the conclusions reached in these books. The twelve zodiac signs and their ancient astrological lore are found to encode a physics that describes the spontaneous explosive creation of matter and energy.[3] Furthermore, using constellation pointers, the zodiac indicates the Galactic center as the location of this energetic outburst. That is, according to star lore mythology, Sagittarius (The Archer) is aiming his arrow tip (Gamma Sagittarii) at the Heart of the Scorpion which is specifically represented by Alpha Scorpii, a bright red supergiant star. Regressing these star positions back in time, we find that the Archer's arrow shaft would have been precisely aligned with the Scorpion's Heart around 14,000 B.C. With this trajectory sighting, Sagittarius' arrow indicates the location of the Galactic core to within 0.35° of arc (figure 21). Knowing further that Sagittarius and Scorpio together represent

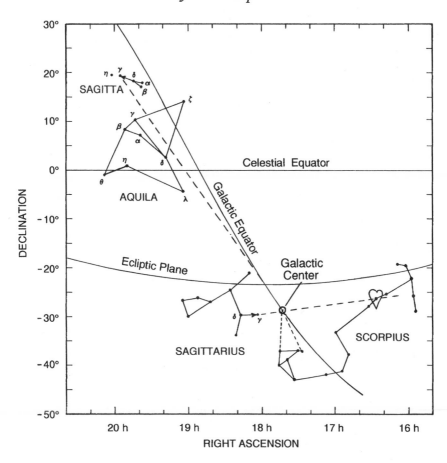

Figure 21. A sky map showing the locations of the constellations of Sagittarius, Scorpius, Sagitta, and Aquila (from LaViolette, *Beyond the Big Bang*, figure 9.20).

archetypal symbols for the first emergence of this created matter and energy, the arrow indication along with its encoded date, would record a time when a Galactic center outburst became apparent to Earth observers — the date when this energy volley began passing through the solar system.

Sagitta, the Celestial Arrow, which is portrayed flying away from the Galactic center with its point close to the northern Galactic one-radian point, is Sagittarius' arrow, which has been explosively eject-ed from the Heart of the Scorpion, or in other words, from the exploding Galactic center. Considering that the arrow tip, Gamma Sagittae, is the closest constellation star to the northern Galactic one-radian point, the Celestial Arrow symbolically represents an energetic volley of cosmic ray particles and electromagnetic radiation that originated from the Galactic center and traveled radially outward the 23,000 light year distance from the Galactic center to our solar system. Recall that an arc beginning at the Galactic center and extending outward in the plane of the sky over an angle of one radian has a length equal to the distance from the Galactic center to the Earth.

This raises the question that, by designating this same one radian concept, perhaps the one-radian pulsar clump "arrow" and the millisecond pulsar beacons, PSR 1937+21 and PSR 1957+20, are all referring to this same Galactic explosion event. Indeed, if an astronomical phenomenon of this sort had occurred, it would indeed be the "talk of the Galaxy," the phenomenon that extraterrestrial communications would most likely be discussing since it is something that *all civilizations in the Milky Way have experienced in common*.

Galactic Superwaves

Earth Under Fire presents astronomical and geological evidence indicating that a protracted global climatic disaster did occur shortly after this 14,000 year B.C. date. These findings suggest that, about every 13 to 26 thousand years, the immense radiant mass at the core of our Galaxy enters an explosive phase which lasts up to several thousand years during which it produces a fierce wind of cosmic ray particles and electromagnetic radiation. This forms an expanding spherical shell of radiation called a *superwave* that travels radially outward from the Galactic nucleus at close to the speed of light and penetrates entirely through and beyond the surrounding spiral arm disk (figure 22).[4,5]

Since the mid 1960's astronomers have known that the massive cores of galaxies periodically enter a quasar-like active phase during which they intensely radiate cosmic ray particles and electromagnetic emissions. In 1983 when I first proposed the superwave concept, astronomers were assuming that galactic core explosions occur much less frequently, about every hundred million years, and that their expelled particles were trapped within a few hundred light years of the galaxy's nucleus. Although, in some cases, where long range propagation was evident, they assumed the particles were confined to narrow beams. I demonstrated this was incorrect, observational evidence indicating that outbursts occurred far more

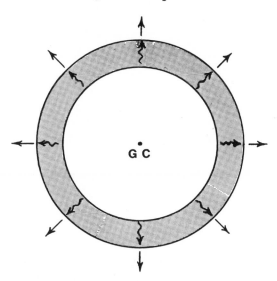

Figure 22. A schematic representation of a Galactic superwave. Cosmic ray particles and electromagnetic radiation move radially outward from the Galactic center in the form of an expanding shell (from LaViolette, *Earth Under Fire*, figure 3.1).

frequently, their expelled cosmic rays traveling radially outward to penetrate the entire Galaxy. Radio telescope observations of the Galactic center recently confirmed this model of long-range radial propagation with the discovery that synchrotron radiation from our Galactic core is mainly *circularly* polarized.[6] Circularly polarized synchrotron radiation is produced when cosmic rays travel *toward the observer at close to the speed of light,* following a spiral trajectory. Hence they would be traveling radially away from the Galactic center.

As a superwave sweeps through the Galaxy, it has a major effect on the numerous sun-like star systems it encounters. Normally, the continual outward sweeping action of a star's ion wind is able to keep its immediate environment clear of interstellar dust. However, at times when a reasonably intense superwave cosmic ray volley is passing by and is sustained over a period of many centuries, dust and gas residing near a star would be pushed forward and would acquire sufficient momentum to invade the star's planetary environment. As this material penetrated inward and fell under the influence of the star's gravitational pull, much of it ultimately would crash onto the star's surface with great force. The released energy would add to that which the star generates internally, thereby causing its luminosity to increase. Energy would also be supplied to the star's surface from its newly acquired dust shroud. This would intercept a considerable fraction of the star's outgoing visible light and return a portion back toward the star. Both of these effects together would energize the star's surface and induce it to engage in violent flaring activity. This enhanced flaring could expose any planets in the star's solar system to high levels of radiation that would be hazardous for any life they might support.

The presence of this interplanetary dust would also substantially alter the climate of such planets, less radiation coming directly from the star and more coming indirectly as scattered or reradiated light. This indirect component would have warmed a planet relatively uniformly as though it were in a hothouse. This warming would have had its greatest effect in the polar regions of a planet since these normally receive little direct radiation due to the low angle of incidence there. So, a planet's polar regions would have tended to become warmer than normal.

In addition, since the dust would absorb a portion of the star's light and reradiate it as infrared, the star's spectrum would have become reddened, thereby changing the amount of energy that would penetrate to the surface of the planet through its atmosphere. Together with the enhanced radiation output from the star, these effects could either induce climatic warmings or climatic coolings, the net result being dependent upon the magnitude of these various radiation processes and the radiation absorption properties of the planet's atmosphere. Calculations performed for our own planet demonstrate that the climatic impact would be quite sizable, sufficient to either initiate an ice age or end an existing glacial period depending on the circumstances.[7]

Astronomical and geological evidence suggests that the most recent major superwave passed our solar system toward the end of the last ice age.[8] This is corroborated by ice core data from Byrd Station, Antarctica which indicates that the intensity of Galactic cosmic ray radiation striking the Earth's atmosphere rose to moderate levels around 16,000 years ago, reached a peak around $14,150 \pm 200$ years ago, again around $13,300 \pm 200$ years ago, and climaxed a third time around $12,700 \pm 200$ years ago (see lower profile in figure 23).[9] The last phase, the most prolonged of the three, lasted for about 1500 years, all three peaks spanning a period of about 3000 years. This period of elevated cosmic ray intensity coincided with the climatic warming trend that ultimately ended the

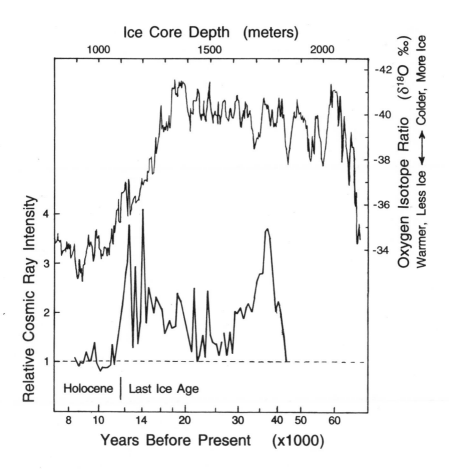

Figure 23. Lower profile: Cosmic ray intensity impacting the solar system (0 – 40 kyrs B.P.) normalized to present levels. [Based on the Byrd Station ice core [10]Be concentration data of Beer et al. (*Nuc. Instrum. Meth. Phys. Res.*, p. 204, and *The Last Deglaciation*, p. 145], adjusted by the Author for changes in ice accumulation rate and solar wind screening.) Upper profile: The ice core's oxygen isotope ratio, and indicator of ambient temperature and glacial ice sheet size (courtesy of W. Dansgaard).

ice age (see upper isotope profile in figure 23). This graph, which plots cosmic ray intensity normalized to present day intensities, was constructed from measurements of the concentration of beryllium-10 ([10]Be) present in polar ice. [10]Be is a medium half-life element produced by the collision of high-energy cosmic rays with nitrogen in our atmosphere. Consequently, by determining the rate at which

[10]Be was being produced in the atmosphere and subsequently accumulating on the Earth's surface, one may determine the intensity with which galactic cosmic ray radiation was impacting the Earth. Furthermore by estimating solar flare activity levels in the past, one may determine the degree to which the solar wind was impeding the entry of galactic cosmic rays, making it possible to infer the unattenuated intensity at which the incident cosmic ray barrage was impacting the solar system.

Lunar rock data show that the period at the end of the last ice age (16,000 − 10,000 years B.P.) was distinguished by intense solar flaring activity.*[10-13] As mentioned earlier, this extreme activity would have been induced by the high concentrations of cosmic dust brought into the solar system by the impacting superwave. Also, geologic records indicate that the Earth's ice age climate began warming on a global scale around 15,800 years ago with a dramatic change beginning around 14,700 years ago, when temperatures in high latitude regions reached near present day values for almost two thousand years.[14] This was accompanied by a period of rapid ice sheet melting and continental flooding. There is no known terrestrial mechanism that can account for such a rapid warming of the whole planet! However, such a climatic shift would have been an expected consequence of an activated Sun and dust congested interplanetary medium.

Moreover excess radiocarbon levels found in ice age sediments indicate that solar activity reached a peak around 12,750 years ago,[15] a time that coincides with the worst episode of mass animal extinction to occur in millions of years.[16] Together with the lunar rock evidence, this suggests that the Earth and Moon were engulfed by a highly intense solar coronal mass ejection which exposed the Earth's surface to lethal radiation levels. This prolonged disaster may have spawned myths and legends describing celestial phenomena where a previously darkened Sun violently erupts to singe the Earth and trigger the release of vast deluges that wash over the land, events that are said to have nearly extinguished the human race.

The graph shown in figure 24, which plots data from the Vostok ice core, presents a longer term view of the relative cosmic ray intensity that has been striking the solar system.[17] As in figure 23, the cosmic ray intensity plotted here was determined from measurements of [10]Be accumulation rate and from estimates of solar flare

---

* B.P. signifies "before present," as referenced from the year 1950 AD.

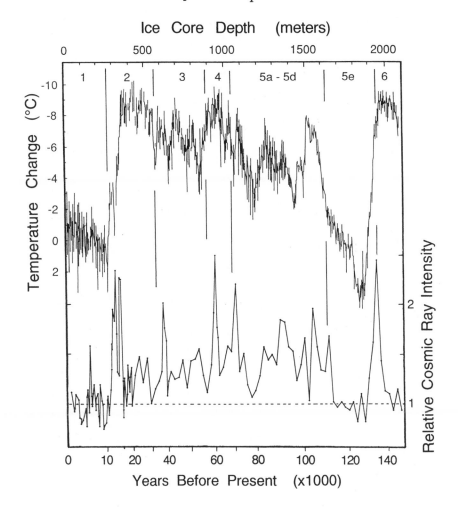

Figure 24. Lower profile: Cosmic ray intensity impacting the solar system (0 – 145 kyrs B.P.) normalized to present levels (based on the Vostok, Antarctica ice core ^{10}Be concentration data of Raisbeck et al. [*The Last Deglaciation*, p. 130], adjusted by the Author for changes in ice accumulation rate and solar wind screening). Upper profile: Ambient air temperature, as indicated by the ice core's deuterium content (from Jouzel, *Nature*, p. 403).

activity. The data indicates that several large galactic cosmic ray events occurred during the last ice age which dates from 110,000 to 11,600 years ago. Also another large peak about 132,000 years ago is apparent at the end of the preceding ice age. The peaks at 14,200 ± 200 years ago and at 12,650 ± 200 years ago are seen to be the most recently occurring of the major cosmic ray events, although a very brief small scale event may have occurred around 5350 years ago (figure 24).

The cosmic ray peak dating from around 37,000 years B.P. has received a considerable amount of attention since it has been detected in several ice core records. The scientific community has reached a consensus that this peak indeed represents a period of enhanced cosmic ray intensity. However, the ice core record contains other equally prominent peaks. Galactic superwaves can recur often enough to explain them, whereas nearby supernova explosions occur far too infrequently. In particular, there is independent astronomical data to corroborate the passage of a superwave during the period from 15,000 to 11,000 years B.P.[18, 19]

The corresponding cosmic ray peaks at the end of the last ice age are not readily discerned from the raw ^{10}Be concentration ice core data. Hence their presence has until now eluded ice core researchers and as a result they have received no discussion in the scientific literature. Their presence becomes apparent only when the raw data is properly adjusted to take account of past changes in ice accumulation rate and in the degree of solar wind screening.* That is, a rise in annual snowfall increases the ice accumulation rate and

---

* The cosmic ray intensity peaks seen in figure 24 at the end of the last ice age (11,000 to 15,000 years B.P.) appear much more prominent and clearly defined than they do in a similar Vostok cosmic ray profile that was published earlier in the first edition of *Earth Under Fire* (figure 3.8). One difference is that the above updated profile includes more data points in the period of interest from 0 to 20,000 years before present. Also, in producing this profile, data values for the period 15,000 to 10,000 years B.P., which represent the intensity of galactic cosmic rays striking the Earth, were adjusted upward substantially so that the profile would accurately represent the cosmic ray intensity impacting the solar system. This upward adjustment is necessary since ^{14}C data indicates that solar flare activity was at least an order of magnitude greater during that period and hence that the solar wind would have had a substantially greater screening effect on the incident cosmic ray flux. No similar solar wind adjustments were made to earlier cosmic ray peaks due to insufficient data on solar activity that far back in time. Another distinguishing improvement, the present cosmic ray profile is based on a more accurate determination of the atmospheric ^{10}Be production rate for the upper portion of the Vostok ice core. That is, by using a new, more detailed ice core climatic profile for the period 20,000 years B.P. to the present, it was possible to more accurately date the Vostok core through correlation with the well-dated Summit, Greenland ice core profile. This, in turn, allowed the rates of ice accumulation and ^{10}Be production to be more accurately determined. Details of the derivation of the profiles shown in figures 23 and 24 are described in a technical paper (LaViolette, 1999).

yields greater ^{10}Be dilution hence lower ^{10}Be concentrations. Also, greater solar wind screening results in lower ^{10}Be concentrations.

Although scientists have today amassed a considerable store of knowledge about galactic core explosions seen happening in the nuclei of distant galaxies and have gathered evidence that such outbursts have also poured forth from the center of our own Galaxy, still the superwave phenomenon is quite elusive. The quiescent periods between outbursts are so long that any knowledge of the previous event would be long forgotten, surviving only in scattered myths that report some of the terrestrial consequences. The cosmic ray electron volley leaves little hint of its presence in the Galaxy once it has passed. The electrons themselves are invisible, their presence being evidenced only through the synchrotron radiation they emit. But since they beam their radiation away from the Galactic center, their emission is not easily discerned once the superwave has passed the observer. Moreover, due to their speed-of-light flight through the Galaxy, subsequent superwaves would arrive with little warning. It appears that some ancient civilization attempted to bridge this long gap in time by sending us a time capsule message with the purpose of warning future generations about the phenomenon. Indeed, were it not for this ancient message embedded within constellation lore, we might not today have known about the superwave's past attack.

Could the pulsar network be referring to this same galactic cosmic ray phenomenon? Just like the constellation cipher in ancient terrestrial star lore, the pulsar signals beamed in our direction explicitly refer to the northern Galactic one-radian point as seen from our particular Galactic location. In so doing, they not only imply that they have knowledge of the one-radian geometrical concept, but also that they know the location of the Galactic center and that events happening at this central location affect our solar system. Moreover, like our own constellation lore which places one pointer near the northern one-radian point (the Sagitta arrow), another near the Galactic center (the Sagittarius arrow), and another near the southern one-radian point (the Crucis cross), the pulsar network also refers to these three key locations by placing eclipsing binary pulsars near each site.

It should not be entirely a surprise to find that this last superwave is the topic of interstellar conversation. Indeed, all worlds in the Galaxy must endure the consequences of a superwave's passage. In choosing a subject for interstellar communication, it makes sense that another civilization would select a phenomenon that we and other civilizations in our direction would have similarly experienced. Just as a volcanic eruption or major earthquake becomes the subject for widespread discussion on the evening news. So too, we can expect that the most recent superwave would be a prime topic for conversation in interstellar ETI transmissions.

There are also altruistic motives that would encourage interstellar conversation about superwaves. The more advanced civilizations in the Galaxy might warn others who are less informed about past occurrences of this phenomenon. Or they might even share information about when the next superwave would arrive, perhaps conveying information about this through the Galactic network by transmitting signals that travel far faster than light. They might also explain ways in which a civilization might protect itself from a superwave attack, for example, by devising ways of deflecting the trajectories of approaching cosmic rays.

Given that highly unique pulsar beacons have sky positions so close to that of the key constellation star Gamma Sagittae, the speculation comes to mind that the Sagitta constellation and the zodiac constellation lore with its encoded time capsule cipher might all be of extraterrestrial origin. This "ancient astronaut" theory suggests that, shortly after the decimating passage of the last major superwave, our planet was visited by advanced beings from a nearby star system whose civilization was a communicating member of the pulsar network. They could conceivably have devised a constellation lore for Earth's survivors whose purpose was to inform future generations about this catastrophe and about the superwave that caused it. In so doing, they could have arranged that this time capsule message and the Galactic pulsar network message would cross-reference one another.

In fact, there are indications that whoever designed the zodiac constellation lore possessed *a very advanced knowledge of science*. For example, when we consider the trajectory of the Archer's arrow sighting toward the Heart of the Scorpion, consider also the location of the Sagitta arrow at its position close to the northern Galactic one-radian point, and the location of the Southern Cross marker, Crucis, which accurately indicates the southern Galactic one-radian point, we must conclude that whoever configured this system of asterisms must have known the location of the Galactic center to within a few tenths of a degree of arc. Modern scientists have bettered this accuracy only in recent decades by using large-dish radio telescopes.

Also, the zodiac symbolically designates a temperature gradient in space that extends progressively from a hot pole in the direction of Leo to a cool pole in the direction of Aquarius. Modern scientists confirmed this only recently when they discovered a similar dipole temperature anisotropy in the 3° Kelvin cosmic microwave background radiation.[20] They accomplished this through the use of stratospheric flight, sophisticated electronic circuitry, and cryogenically cooled microwave detectors.

In addition, a considerable amount of scientific knowledge was apparently involved in crafting the Virgo constellation and its lore. Myths describe her as seeding stars throughout the universe. The actual constellation shows her pointing to the center of the Virgo supercluster with her right hand while scattering stars out along the supercluster equator with her left hand.[21] The Virgo supercluster is the largest collection of galaxies in our part of the universe, our own galactic cluster being an outlying member. To be aware of the uniqueness of this location, an ancient civilization would have needed to have access to an optical telescope capable of resolving the images of distant galaxies, a telescope having an aperture of at least 6 inches. Moreover their science would have had to be sufficiently advanced to have a knowledge of galactic redshift spectra, thereby allowing them to understand that the images they were seeing were distant galaxies and not local gas clouds.

Ancient writings do refer to sightings of advanced airborne craft and of past contact with extraterrestrial beings.[22,23] Viewed within a historical context that acknowledges the existence of such contact, the notion that ancient terrestrial star lore might interface with a message symbolically conveyed through a network of interstellar communication beacons does not seem all that far fetched.

Chapter 5

Superwave Warning Beacons

The Crab and Vela Supernova Remnants

There is another part of the pulsar message that makes even more explicit reference to the Galactic cosmic ray volley that passed the Earth at the end of the last ice age. It is conveyed by the Crab and Vela pulsars, two very unusual pulsars that are not found near the one-radian points. One important characteristic that distinguishes them from most others is that they are both associated with supernova remnants. As we shall see, this supernova connection is crucial to understanding their superwave message.

The Crab pulsar (PSR 0531+21) is associated with the Crab Nebula supernova remnant (figure 25), which lies near the outer edge of the Milky Way in the constellation of Taurus, the Bull. Our solar system lies about 23,000 light years from the Galactic center, and the Crab Nebula is situated 6585 light years further out, the Galaxy having a radius of roughly 35,000 light years. The Crab supernova was observed by Chinese astronomers in 1054 AD, making it one of the few bright supernovae to occur in the last millennium.

The Vela pulsar (PSR 0833-45) lies along the line of sight of the Vela supernova remnant which is situated just 820 ± 100 light years away in the constellation of Vela, The Sail. The date of the Vela supernova is not known as well as that of the Crab, since it occurred so long ago. But astronomers often give its age to be in the range of 10,000 to 12,000 years old.[1] Sumerian star lore tells of a "giant star" (i.e., supernova) that once appeared in the constellation of Vela which it identifies with the god Ea, the Lord of the Waters.[2] The Sumarians regarded Ea as the god of Wisdom who taught humanity the arts of civilization. More significantly, their flood myth states that Ea was the god who warned Ziusudra (Noah) of the impending flood disaster that was about to drown the world. The geologic record indicates several times at the end of the last ice age when the ice sheets were rapidly melting and flooding the land, but the most significant of these events is the one that occurred $10,750 \pm 100$ B.C.

Figure 25. Image of the Crab Nebula with a time sequence inset showing the Crab pulsar's optical pulses over the course of one cycle. Each of the 33 time slices represents an interval of approximately one millisecond. The pulsar's brighter main pulse is visible in the first column; its less intense, broader interpulse can be seen in the second column. Kitt Peak National Observatory (courtesy of N. Sharp, AURA, NOAO, and NSF; Sharp, *P.A.S.P.*, figure 9).

which marks the time of the terminal Pleistocene mass extinction. A study of animal remains indicates that this disaster was indeed associated with cataclysmic floods that occurred on a global scale.[3] If this is the global flood that Sumerian legend describes, then the day's of Ea and the associated Vela supernova might be dated back to that same period, circa 10,750 B.C., which corresponds reasonably well with accepted estimates for the age of this remnant. Since the Vela supernova occurred relatively close to the solar system, it would have been quite bright and could have made quite an impression on ice age cultures.

Pulsars Are Not Made in Supernova Explosions

Conventional theory assumes that pulsars are spinning neutron stars that have been born out of the crushing pressures of a super-nova explosion. The vast majority of the more than 1100 known pulsars exhibit no supernova remnant associations, and astronomers presume this is because they are so old that their supernova remnants have long since dissipated. But if the neutron star theory were correct, neutron stars should be found within the 200 known supernova remnants, and even if their synchrotron beams are not aimed in our direction, they should make themselves evident from the X-rays their hot surfaces would be radiating in all directions. However, as of the time of writing, *only 10 supernova remnants* have been found to be associated with pulsars. As for the other remnants, X-ray telescope observations have turned up little evidence of compact energetic X-ray sources. So we are left with a mere 10 detections out of a possible 200.

The paucity of pulsar detections in the observable set of remnants has been disturbing to pulsar astronomers. For example, in their 1986 review paper, pulsar astronomers Joseph Taylor and Dan Stinebring wonder:

> Why, among the ~150 known galactic supernova remnants, have pulsars been found in only three? Even at a few hundred kilometers per second, pulsar velocities are much less than the several thousand kilometers per second typical of supernova ejecta. Therefore a pulsar created in a supernova event should remain well inside the supernova remnant as long as the remnant is visible, and it should be relatively easy to find. Efforts to find such pulsars have not been very successful.[4]

Among those pulsars that are found within the perimeter of a supernova remnant, there is still a question as to whether they in fact originated from the remnant's supernova explosion. The Vela pulsar is one example. It is located at (ℓ = 263.55°, b = -2.79°), about 1.3° of arc from the center of the 5° diameter Vela supernova remnant located at (ℓ = 263.9 ± 0.2°, b = -1.8 ± 0.2°). If we assume that the Vela pulsar lies as far away as the Vela remnant (820 light years), the pulsar would lie 18 light years from the remnant explosion center. To have traveled this far in the time that has elapsed since the occurrence of the Vela supernova, the pulsar would have had to be traveling at a speed of 450 kilometers per second. Instead, measurements of the pulsar's proper motion show it to be moving *at only about one fifth of this speed* and along a trajectory that is *not* aligned with this explosion site.[5,6] This may be seen in figure 26 which charts coordinates for the central portion of the remnant.

A similar problem arises regarding the Crab pulsar (figure 27).

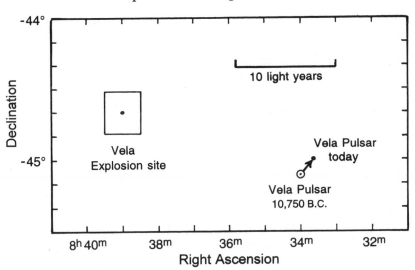

Figure 26. Location and trajectory of the Vela pulsar as compared with the location of the Vela supernova explosion site.

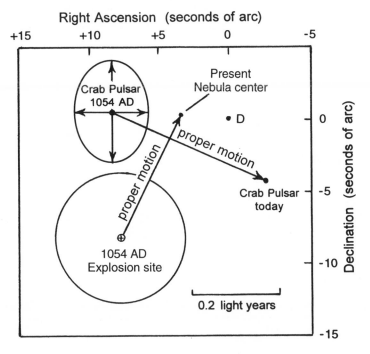

Figure 27. Location and trajectory of the Crab pulsar compared with the location of the Crab supernova explosion site. Map coordinates are referenced to star D (after Trimble, *Astronomical Journal*, figure 2).

As viewed in the plane of the sky, the Crab pulsar is currently located at (ℓ = 184.56°, b = -5.78°), about 0.35 light years from the site of the Crab supernova explosion.[7] Knowing the pulsar's proper motion from recent data,[8] we can project back in time to find the position that the pulsar would have had in 1054 AD, the date of the supernova. In fact, we find that on this date its location *misses the supernova remnant explosion center by about 0.3 light years*. Also the pulsar is not found to be traveling radially away from this center, like the expanding nebular material, but instead is moving perpendicular to this direction. Furthermore, *it is doubtful that the Crab pulsar is located inside the nebula* because if it were its radio signal dispersion should be decreasing 0.07% per year as the nebula's plasma expands and thins out. Observations show that the pulsar's dispersion is instead increasing.[9] So, we come to a conclusion similar to that for the Vela pulsar: namely, we find *no evidence to suggest that the Crab pulsar originated from the Crab supernova explosion*. Considering the general scarcity of pulsar-supernova remnant associations, we are left to doubt the currently popular model that pulsars are formed in supernova explosions.

Is it then just due to chance that the Crab and Vela pulsars are associated with their respective remnants? Or, could these flashing signals be ETI beacons whose positions and signaling directions have been carefully chosen to mark these remnants for us? If so, for what reason would they be marked, and why these particular remnants? One clue comes from noting the locations of the remnants, both of which are found to have unique positions relative to our solar system. The Vela remnant, for example, is the *second closest* supernova remnant to us, lying just 820 light years away (figure 28). It is surpassed in proximity to our solar system by the North Polar Spur, a several million year old remnant whose explosion center is located about 400 light years from us.

The more distant Crab Nebula remnant has the distinction of being the only remnant to have a sky position *so close to the Galactic anticenter*, the direction that lies exactly opposite to the Galactic center direction, and whose position relative to background stars depends specifically on the viewer's location in the galactic disk. The center of the Crab Nebula is positioned at the galactic longitude and latitude position (184.56°, -5.78°), just 7.4° from the Galactic anticenter position (179.94°, 0.05°); see figure 28. Being just 946 years old as of the year 2000, the Crab would be classified as a young remnant, and among the class of young remnants it holds

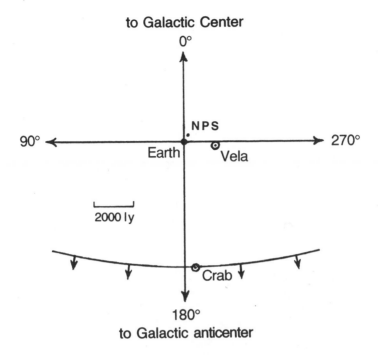

Figure 28. The positions of the Crab and Vela supernova explosions relative to the solar system.

the honor of being the *closest to our solar system.*

The Crab Nebula also happens to be the most conspicuous supernova remnant in the sky. Unlike most remnants which require radio telescope observation to reveal their presence, the Crab Nebula is optically visible. It is the only one that can be easily seen with an amateur optical telescope. Is it just a coincidence that, of all supernova remnants in the Galaxy, the two that happen to have such unique placements relative to our solar system should be among the few to be marked with pulsars, and as we shall see, by two very unusual pulsars?

Wave of Destruction

Supernova Triggering by Superwaves. To discover why these remnants might have been chosen to be marked with ETI communication beacons, we must look beyond merely the fact that they are uniquely placed relative to us. As we shall see, both of

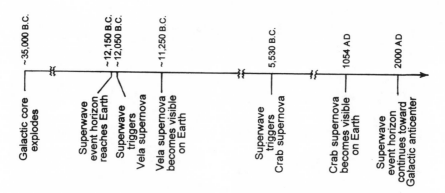

Figure 29. Event time-line for the sequential triggering of the Vela and Crab supernova explosions.

these supernovae appear to have been triggered by the same Galactic superwave that was responsible for the major cataclysm at the end of the last ice age. When we take account of the remnants' locations in the Galaxy and their ages, we find that their respective supernovae were asynchronously linked with one another, their detonation dates differing approximately by the amount of time it takes light to travel from the Vela site to the Crab site! It is, then, entirely reasonable that a superwave "event horizon," moving outward from the Galactic center at the speed of light and reaching the Earth around 14,130 years ago, first passed the relatively nearby Vela site, causing its supernova to occur, and then after traveling some 6300 light years further on, passed the Crab Nebula site causing its supernova also to occur (figures 28 and 29). [10,11]

A particularly intense superwave could have coaxed the progenitor stars of these various remnants to explode if these stars were hot, inherently unstable, and embedded in a dust-laden environment. [12-14] That is, upon their arrival, the superwave cosmic rays would overpower the star's stellar wind and push nearby dust in close to the star. As the star begins to gravitationally draw this material onto its surface, the added kinetic energy would provoke its energy output to rise abruptly, whereupon the star would finally explode. Alternatively, an advancing superwave might carry a steep gravitational field gradient that could induce frictional tidal forces sufficiently strong to energize the star and cause it to explode.

Since the Crab supernova was seen less than a thousand years ago, the superwave that triggered its explosion should still be in the remnant's vicinity impacting it with cosmic ray electrons. The ionized turbulent plasma within the remnant would be magnetically trapping these impacting particles, capturing them into tight spiral orbits and causing them to continuously emit synchrotron radiation in all directions. This explains why the entire remnant is presently seen to be an intense emitter of synchrotron radiation at radio, optical, and X-ray wavelengths. At optical, X-ray, and gamma ray wavelengths it is the *brightest* supernova remnant in the sky and at radio wavelengths it is the second brightest. Astronomers concur that this emission is produced by cosmic ray electrons trapped in the remnant.

Being unaware of the superwave phenomenon, astrophysicists have concluded that the cosmic rays illuminating the Crab Nebula are being supplied from the Crab pulsar which they presume lies inside the remnant. However, the majority of cosmic rays producing this emission should be coming from the passing superwave and *not from the pulsar*.

If the electrons producing the nebula's radio and optical emission were coming exclusively from the pulsar, then the synchrotron emission coming from the Crab Nebula and from its pulsar should be found to have very similar differential energy flux spectra. But they don't. In the radio and optical spectral regions, the Crab remnant and Crab pulsar spectra have entirely different slopes, indicating that they are produced by *different* populations of cosmic rays.[15-17] The Crab Nebula's synchrotron optical spectrum is negatively sloped, decreases in intensity with increasing frequency, whereas the Crab pulsar's optical spectrum is instead positively sloped. The Crab Nebula and Crab pulsar both have synchrotron radio spectra that are negatively sloped, but the pulsar's radio spectrum is 10 times steeper than that of the nebula, a slope of - 2.5, as compared with - 0.26 for the nebula. The Crab Nebula's radio spectrum makes a far better match to the nonthermal spectrum of the *Galactic radio background radiation* which has a slope of -0.4, a diffuse emission that astronomers agree is produced by Galactic cosmic rays.* This diffuse synchrotron radiation comes from all parts of the sky, but is more concentrated toward the galactic plane and rises to its maximum intensity toward the Galactic center. More specifically, as I have shown in my dissertation, this radio

---

* The Galactic radio background should not be confused with the cosmic microwave background radiation, which instead has a thermal blackbody spectrum and is instead of intergalactic origin.

Figure 30. A radio contour map of the Crab Nebula showing the intensity of its synchrotron radio emission. The arrow indicates the position of the Crab pulsar (Reprinted courtesy of NRAO, *Nature* magazine, and T. Velusamy, *Nature*, figure 2).

background radiation is accurately modeled by a shell of superwave cosmic rays moving outward at the 12,150 B.C. superwave event horizon. A contour map of this radiation shows that the observed radio intensity varies with galactic longitude in the same way as would be expected if produced by these superwave cosmic rays.

Among the category of young supernova remnants, there are two others whose, ages, locations, and distances from us are accurately known — the Cassiopeia A and Tycho remnants. Like the Crab remnant, we find that these also are in the midst of the superwave particle barrage. The locations of these remnants in relation to the superwave may be seen in figure 31 which adopts a view looking down onto the galactic plane. The superwave event horizon does not plot out as a sphere, but rather as an ellipsoid with foci centered at the Galactic center and at the Earth. All points on this horizon are

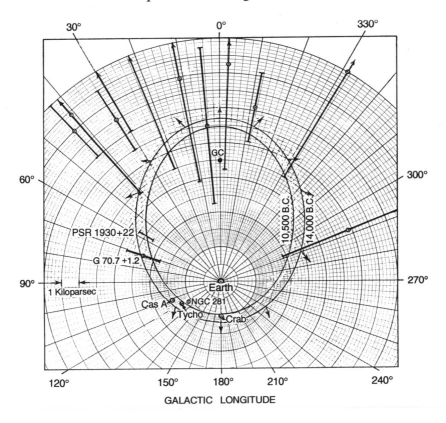

Figure 31. The positions of several young supernova remnants relative to event horizons for superwaves passing the solar system 12,500 and 16,000 years ago. Cosmic ray intensity would have peaked about midway between these two boundaries. The galactic plane lies in the plane of the paper. GC indicates the location of the Galactic center (P. LaViolette, *Earth Under Fire*, figure 10.4).

determined by the sum of: 1) the time required for superwave cosmic rays to travel from the Galactic center outward to that horizon, and 2) the time required for synchrotron radiation from that horizon to travel back toward the Earth at the speed of light and be seen by us (see *Earth Under Fire* for an explanation).

The timing of the Tycho and Cassiopeia A supernova explosions suggests that they were triggered by the same superwave front that triggered the Vela and Crab explosions. Taking into consideration the time required for the shell of superwave cosmic rays to cover the galactic radial distance from our solar system to the site of the Crab supernova (6,520 years), the time for light from the resulting

TABLE 2

Indication that a Single Superwave Triggered Four Supernovae

Remnant	Distance from Us	Date of Visible Explosion	Earth Passage Date of Superwave
Crab	6,585 ± 30 l.y.	1054 AD	12,050 ± 60 B.C.
Cas A	9,450 ± 300 l.y.	1658 AD	12,720 ± 500 B.C.
Tycho	8,150 ± 300 l.y.	1572 AD	11,610 ± 500 B.C.
Vela	820 ± 100 l.y.	10,750 ± 2000 B.C.	11,670 ± 2000 B.C.
Average of Crab, Cas A, & Tycho:			12,130 ± 600 B.C.

supernova explosion to travel back to the Earth (6585 years), and the datewhen this supernova was seen on Earth (1054 AD), we find that the event horizon triggering this explosion should have passed through the solar system around 12,050 ± 60 B.C. (see Table 2).[18]

Performing the same calculation for the Cas A and Tycho remnants we find dates of 12,720± 500 B.C. and 11,610± 500 B.C. respectively. Averaging together the Crab, Cas A, and Tycho dates, gives 12,130 ± 600 B.C. as the best estimate for the time when the most intense part of the Galactic superwave would have passed the Earth. This compares favorably with the event horizon date of 11,670 ± 2000 B.C. that would have been responsible for triggering the Vela supernova. This also correlates reasonably well with the 12,150 B.C. climax in galactic cosmic ray intensity registered in the Earth's polar ice core records. So we are left to conclude that *all of these supernovae were triggered by the same Galactic superwave event horizon,* whose Earth passage date is marked by elevated concentrations of cosmogenic beryllium in polar ice.

In view of the above, we are led to wonder whether the Crab and Vela pulsars are ETI beacons that were carefully positioned at the sites of the Crab and Vela supernovae to call our attention to the most recent Galactic superwave event, one that was involved in triggering these explosions. Of the various supernovae that this superwave triggered, the remnant of the Vela explosion is closest of all to the Earth. Also, the remnant of the 1054 AD Crab explosion is closest of all to the Galactic anticenter location. So, by specifically marking these particular remnants, a Galactic collective would be conveying the idea of a disturbance moving away from the Galactic

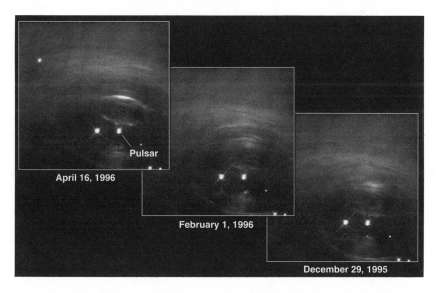

Figure 32. Successive images of the Crab nebula made with the Hubble Space Telescope showing changes in the luminous wisps in the vicinity of the pulsar. The image has been rotated counterclockwise so that the nebula's long axis is disposed vertically (courtesy of J. Hester, P. Scowen, and NASA).

center at close to the speed of light.

Superwave Bow Shock Fronts. The Crab remnant is unique in that it is the only supernova remnant to show signs of sub-light-speed motion in its interior. This is evident in the rapid movement of *luminous wisps* seen near the Crab pulsar. Figure 32 shows a succession of optical images of the Crab nebula made two months apart with the Hubble Space Telescope. These show substantial activity of the luminous region north of the pulsar (upward in the diagram), where luminous waves are observed to move northward at up to half the speed of light. This motion becomes naturally explained if superwave cosmic rays are traveling face-on toward the remnant (into the diagram) at close to the speed of light and are impacting a bubble-like bow shock front formed around the pulsar (recall figure 19). As the superwave cosmic rays deflect around this obstacle, a large fraction will become magnetically trapped in the shock front and will emit optical synchrotron radiation, seen by us as the luminous wisps.[19]

Since the radiant epicenter of the wisp movement is not centered on the pulsar, but located about 0.15 light years away, astronomers have concluded that this activity must be taking place some distance from the pulsar. Reluctant to relinquish their lighthouse model, they have attempted to attribute the phenomenon to a collimated beam of particles issuing from the pulsar and impacting the surrounding nebula. The beam is assumed to issue along the pulsar's stationary spin axis and to be inclined at a 60 degree angle to our line of sight. However, with such an orientation, the pulsar's synchrotron beam would not be shining in our direction and so we should not be seeing any pulses as the neutron star rotated. So by attempting to account for the wisp activity, the neutron star model runs into difficulty in explaining why we see pulses coming from the Crab pulsar. Rather than indicating activity initiated by the pulsar, this wisp movement instead is most likely caused by the onslaught of waves of superwave cosmic rays that are arriving from the Galactic center and continuously bombarding the Crab Nebula and its pulsar beacon star face-on from our viewing direction.

Astronomers have identified 259 luminous line-emitting gaseous "filaments" in the Crab remnant, and of these three located near the pulsar have very low proper motions. Of these three, the one having the lowest radial velocity ($v \sim 89 \text{ km/s}$), coincides in position with the brighter of the moving luminous wisps seen in figure 32. Consequently, the superwave bow shock front may be forming around both the pulsar and this unusually stationary filament.

Several studies have been made of the orientation of the Crab Nebula's magnetic field.* These have shown that the magnetic field is oriented quite uniformly across the face of the nebula and in line with the its minor axis, hence perpendicular to the galactic plane.[20] The field maintains a similar orientation even in the vicinity of the pulsar, where it runs roughly parallel to the orientation of the luminous wisps. This suggests that the wisps are regions where the nebula's magnetic field is quite strong and hence better able to trap cosmic rays. Quite significantly, the nebula's magnetic field direction deviates by about 50° from the average field direction in the Crab pulsar that is responsible for producing its optical pulses. This finding has led astronomer William Cocke and his coworkers to conclude that the optical emission from the pulsar and its nebula environment are unrelated:

---

* The orientation of the nebula's magnetic field has been inferred from the direction in which its optical synchrotron emission is polarized. Gyrating electrons always produce synchrotron emission whose plane of polarization is parallel to their gyration plane and perpendicular to the magnetic field direction.

No obvious relation can be detected between the optical polarization of the pulsar and that of the Crab Nebula in its immediate environment.[21]

The lack of similarity between the pulsar and its immediate environment, in regard to both spectrum and polarization direction, provides strong evidence against theories suggesting that the pulsar is actively energizing its nebula, at least at radio and optical wavelengths, and in favor of the idea that most of the nebula's illumination is being externally supplied by a galactic superwave.

There also appears to be evidence of a superwave induced bow shock front around the Cassiopeia A remnant. As seen in figure 33, most of the remnant's synchrotron radio emission comes from its western side (right side in the diagram), the side that faces the Galactic center and the oncoming superwave onslaught.[22-24] Note that this bow shock is displaced westward from the main body of the remnant, as would be expected if the shock surrounds the remnant on the upwind side. The arrows indicate the direction from which the superwave cosmic rays would be approaching in this part of the Galaxy. Given its proximity to the superwave event horizon, it is not surprising to find that Cassiopeia A is *the brightest supernova remnant in the Galaxy at radio wavelengths.*

The Tycho remnant is also quite bright. It ranks as the fourth brightest Galactic supernova remnant at radio wavelengths. Observations of its radio emission spectrum show that its radiation is produced by electrons that match the observed Galactic cosmic ray spectrum.[25] Rather than indicating that supernova explosions are responsible for generating the Galactic cosmic ray background, as some have assumed, this data supports the view that these remnants are being externally energized by cosmic ray electrons that once originated in the core of our Galaxy.

Warning Markers. The Crab and Vela pulsars are among the less than one percent of the pulsar population that are associated with remnants. Further considering that these two remnants number among the group whose explosions appear to have been triggered by the most intense Galactic superwave to pass through in the last 30,000 years, and recognizing the unique locations that the Crab and Vela remnants have relative to us, we can only feel that it is not just a coincidence that we see pulsar flashes coming from these two remnants. The idea strongly suggests itself that the Crab and Vela pulsars were placed in the heavens as *markers* to warn us about this past catastrophe. A precisely timed flashing signal is a universal

Figure 33. Radio contour map of Cassiopeia A made at a radio frequency of 2695 megahertz (adapted from Dickel and Greisen, *Astronomy and Astrophysics*, figure 5). The central cross represents the position of the supernova explosion center. The dashed arc traces out the bow shock front formed by the impacting superwave indicated by the arrows.

archetype on our own planet for conveying a danger warning (e.g., yellow flashing lights for roadside construction hazards). It arouses attention much more effectively than a constant light source. Consequently, a pulsating beacon would be an ideal signal of choice if a Galactic community wished to convey a warning to novice civilizations of the existence of a Galactic danger. The Vela pulsar currently flashes its warning 11.2 times per second and as we approach the superwave event horizon to target the Crab pulsar, we receive a more urgent warning that pulses 29.8 times per second. This warning signal interpretation becomes even more credible when we realize that, of all known pulsars, the Crab and Vela pulsars are the brightest at optical, X-ray, and gamma ray wavelengths and among the top four brightest at radio wavelengths.

Let us now consider these various unique features that make the Vela and Crab pulsars, the "king and queen" of the pulsar family.

The King and Queen of Pulsars

Bright Beacons at All Wavelengths. The Vela and Crab pulsars stand out from the crowd in several respects. First, they both produce very strong radiant energy emissions. At radio frequencies, the Vela pulsar is the brightest pulsar in the sky, outshining the others by several hundred times. The Crab pulsar is the most luminous pulsar in the sky, and also ranks as the fourth brightest when measured at a frequency of 400 megahertz. In addition, both pulsars are unusual in that they emit pulses in the optical, X-ray, and gamma ray regions of the spectrum, where very few pulsars emit detectable amounts of energy. Only one other pulsar besides the Vela and Crab pulsars is known to emit optical pulses, namely the Millisecond Pulsar found at the tip of the one-radian pulsar clump. Also the Vela and Crab pulsars are among the group of just eight pulsars known to emit X-ray pulses and among seven known to emit gamma ray pulses. At gamma ray wavelengths, the Vela pulsar is the brightest source in the sky and the Crab pulsar is the fourth brightest gamma ray pulsar. When all these spectral regions are considered together, the Vela and Crab pulsars are found to be particularly unique in that, among all known pulsars, they are the *only ones* that pulse in all of these spectral regions: radio, optical, X-ray, and gamma ray.

Interpulses. The Crab and Vela pulsars are also distinguished as being among the rare one percent of the pulsar population that produces interpulses, secondary pulses that occur midway between main pulses. The Vela pulsar produces interpulses only at higher energies, in the optical to gamma ray spectral range, whereas the Crab produces them also at radio wavelengths. The Millisecond Pulsar also happens to be one of the few pulse-interpulse beacons.

Giant Pulses. The Crab pulsar is also distinguished as being one of just two pulsars that produce "giant pulses" — radio emission pulses that exceed the average pulse intensity by many fold (see figure 34). The Millisecond Pulsar is the only other pulsar known to produce giant pulses; although those produced by the Crab pulsar are

Figure 34. Stacked sequence of pulses representing 4 hours of observation of the Crab pulsar showing giant pulses. About 92% occur during the main pulse, while the remaining 8 percent surface during the interpulse (courtesy of Gower and Argyle, *The Astrophysical Journal*, figure 1).

far larger. Giant pulses are observed only at radio wavelengths and can rise up to 1600 times the normal pulse intensity.[26] Pulses ten times more intense than the mean recur at about 30 second intervals, while those reaching 100 times the mean intensity recur about once an hour. Thousand fold giant pulses occur much more rarely.

When emitting a giant pulse, the Crab pulsar becomes the brightest radio pulsar in the sky, exceeding even the intensity of the Vela pulsar by up to a few hundred fold. Were it not for this feature, the Crab pulsar would be very difficult to detect at radio frequencies, since the radio emission background coming from its surrounding nebula is a hundred times brighter than its normal radio pulse intensity and so tends to mask the pulsar's signal. In fact, astronomers first discovered the Crab pulsar precisely because of these giant pulses. Considering that the Crab and Millisecond pulsars are the only ones that produce giant pulses and are two of just three that produce optical pulses (the other being the Vela pulsar), we are predisposed to forge a close associative link between them. The one-radian symbolism of the Millisecond Pulsar and the "pulsar clump" connotes an "arrow" flying away from the Galactic center and traveling a distance equal to the radial distance from the Galactic center to our solar system. The associative link established with the Crab pulsar encourages us to carry over this symbolic metaphor to envision the superwave's light-speed flight outward from the Galactic center, passing our solar system close to the time of the Vela supernova, then continuing outward toward the Galactic anticenter where its present position is marked by the recently formed Crab Nebula. On the one hand, we find the giant-pulse-emitting Millisecond Pulsar, through its strategic one-radian location, symbolizing the crest of the superwave's outward flight, and on the other hand, we find the giant-pulse-emitting Crab pulsar currently at the forefront of the outward traveling superwave event horizon.

The Crab pulsar also emits giant pulses during its interpulse phase, although these occur much less frequently than the main pulse giant pulses. One thing that has puzzled lighthouse model theorists is that the interpulse giant pulses do not occur in the same pulse cycle as the main pulse giant pulses, neither are the two correlated in any way. Further confusing the matter, giant pulses are not observed at optical, X-ray, or gamma ray wavelengths, even though the pulsar produces pulses at these high energies in synchrony with its radio pulses. Such "unnatural" behavior is the kind of thing that ET civilizations would try to engineer into their signals so that their communication beacons were not mistaken for natural sources.

Period Glitches. In addition to their intense output over a large portion of the electromagnetic spectrum, the Crab and Vela pulsars are also unusual in that occasionally their precise clock-like pulses can change dramatically. Pulsars normally have extremely constant pulsation periods, predictable to many significant figures, their periods slowly increasing over time at a very constant and predictable rate. However, the Crab and Vela pulsars are among the small percentage, 21 among the known pulsar population, in which this predictable rate of decrease occasionally changes in an abrupt manner. During such a "period glitch," as it is called, the pulsation rate abruptly speeds up and afterward, over a period of several weeks, relaxes back close to its pre-glitch pulsation rate, whereupon the pulsar once again resumes its steady rate of period increase. Figure 35 shows one such period glitch for the Vela pulsar which caused Vela's period to shorten by about one part per million, a change of about 102 billionths of a second. This 1981 glitch was the fifth such event to occur since the pulsar's discovery in 1968. In all, the Vela pulsar experienced nine glitches during the 25 years following its discovery.[27] The Crab pulsar has undergone a similar number of glitches over a comparable period of time, but these have involved much smaller time shifts, of around a billionth of a second.

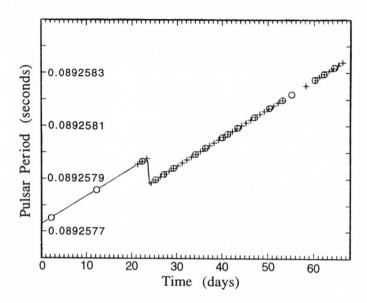

Figure 35. A 102 nanosecond period glitch observed in the Vela pulsar on October 10th, 1981 (after McCulloch, et al., *Nature*, figure 1; by permission from *Nature*, Macmillan Magazines Ltd.).

The uniqueness of the Crab and Vela pulsars goes beyond the fact that they both share this rare glitching phenomenon. The Crab pulsar is distinguished as being the most rapid pulsator of the entire group of glitching pulsars, while Vela ranks as fourth fastest. Depending on which pulsar is studied, there are varying ways in which a glitch and its subsequent period recovery will occur. Yet, the Vela and Crab pulsars happen to have remarkably similar glitch-recovery behaviors. Only one other glitching pulsar exhibits similar behavior, namely PSR 0525+21.[28] But, unlike the Crab and Vela pulsars, PSR 0525+21 is distinguished as having *the longest period of all glitching pulsars*, 3.7455 seconds. Its period ranks third longest of the entire pulsar population. It seems remarkable that the three pulsars that share this distinctly similar glitching behavior should include both the fastest and slowest pulsators among the glitching pulsars (the Crab pulsar and PSR 0525+21).

Even more intriguingly, PSR 0525+21 *just happens to be the Crab pulsar's closest neighbor*. Just a coincidence? We find that it lies about the same distance from Earth as the Crab pulsar and is separated from the Crab pulsar in the plane of the sky by just 1.3 degrees of arc (figure 36). This indicates that the two pulsars are

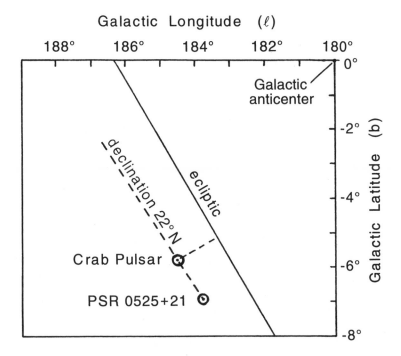

Figure 36. A galactic coordinate map showing the positions of the Crab pulsar and PSR 0525+21. A line projected through them is within 0.01 degrees of being exactly parallel to celestial equator and within a few degrees of paralleling the ecliptic. Their positions coincide with declination 22° north.

separated from one another by just 340 light years. Only one other pulsar is found within 5 degrees of the Crab pulsar, but this lies several thousand light years further away along our line of sight. The probability of two pulsars being located so close together in space and both happening to exhibit the very rare period glitch phenomenon is incredibly small, less than one chance in 10 raised to the 127th power! The chance is even smaller that both would also exhibit similar glitch-recovery behaviors, found in just three of 21 glitching pulsars. The chance is smaller yet that one of this pair would have the shortest period among glitching pulsars, while the other would have the longest period among this glitching subset. The probability that both of these unique pulsars would also be positioned so close to the Galactic anticenter calculates to an even smaller chance.

Period glitches are among the many pulsar signal ordering

characteristics that have confounded astronomers. Working in terms of the troublesome assumption that a pulsar's pulses are produced by the "lighthouse flashes" from a rotating neutron star, theorists have been forced to conclude that a speed-up glitch is produced by a sudden increase in the neutron star's spin rate. They suggest that this "spin-up" might be due to a sudden shrinkage in the neutron star's radius causing, in turn, an abrupt gain in its angular momentum and spin velocity. But how could such a "star quake" occur and not have any major effect on the star's long-term spin-down rate? As seen in figure 35, shortly after the Vela pulsar's glitch, the pulsar's period continued to increase at the same precise rate as before the glitch occurred. How could a pulsar's pulse period be so precisely timed if at any moment this period is capable of undergoing such a drastic change? Current neutron star models are far from providing an adequate explanation. Moreover PSR 0525+21 has presented a particular challenge to lighthouse model theorists since astronomers have concluded that its glitching cannot be due to star quakes and that some other explanation must be sought.

Occasional period glitches make a lot of sense if pulsars are instead extraterrestrial communication beacons. Unusual changes of this sort could be intentionally incorporated both to attract our attention to the pulsar and to confound any attempts we might make to devise a natural explanation. When a repeating signal of such high precision suddenly shifts its period, even by a very small amount, and immediately afterwards resumes its previous precise rate of period increase, this is something that certainly will not be missed by observant astronomers. One other curious discovery, astronomers have found that the Earth is being showered by faint pulses of 100 trillion electron volt cosmic rays coming from this part of the sky and having a period close to that of PSR 0525+21.[29] Is this cosmic ray message a warning to us of things to come?

By itself, the Crab pulsar is quite unique and attention getting. But, seeing another pulsar having such similar glitching properties and positioned so close to it, our interest becomes heightened even more. Furthermore as we shall see shortly, these two pulsars are make special alignments both to the Earth's orbital plane and to its celestial equator. This is one of many "coincidences" relating to the Crab Nebula and Crab pulsar that we will explore in the next chapter.

Chapter 6

Sky Maps of a Celestial Disaster

A Star Chart of the Sagitta Constellation?

Each pulsar has its own unique pulsation period. These can be nearly as small as one thousandth of a second or as long as five seconds, with most being around several tenths of a second in length. In addition, each pulsar has a unique rate at which its characteristic period, P, slowly changes over time, a quantity that is termed the *period derivative*, symbolically represented as dP/dt or alternatively as $\dot{P}$. Period derivatives can range from as small as 0.06 picoseconds per year ($\dot{P} = 1.9 \times 10^{-21}$ seconds per second) to as large as about 47 microseconds per year ($\dot{P} = 1.5 \times 10^{-12}$ seconds per second). Yet, despite these wide ranging values, a pulsar's period changes at an exceedingly constant rate, period derivatives having precisions that reach as high as six significant figures. To see how the various pulsation timing characteristics compare with one another, astronomers sometimes graph a pulsar's period against its period derivative on a logarithmic plot such as that shown in figure 37.

The three pulsar coordinates marked by boxes in the upper left hand corner of the graph plot the logarithmic period and period-derivative coordinates ($\log P - \log \dot{P}$) for the Crab pulsar, Vela pulsar, and Vulpecula pulsar (PSR 1930+22). All three are associated with supernova remnants, and all three are relatively fast pulsars with periods of 33.4, 89.3, and 144.5 milliseconds respectively. Interestingly, the layout of the coordinates for these three pulsars calls to mind the appearance of the Sagitta star constellation. Identify galactic longitude, $\ell°$, with log P, where log P is instead plotted to increase from right to left in figure 37, and then compare figure 37 with figure 18 in which galactic longitude similarly increases from right to left. Also identify galactic latitude with log $\dot{P}$ where b° becomes increasingly negative with decreasing log $\dot{P}$ (top to bottom in figure 37). The relative spacing of the three $P - \dot{P}$ points and their

Figure 37. Pulsar period *P* (horizontal axis) plotted against pulsar period derivative *Ṗ* (vertical axis) on a logarithmic graph for 305 pulsars (after Dewey et al., *The Astrophysical Journal*, figure 2b). The squares mark the coordinates for the Crab, Vela, and Vulpecula pulsars.

alignment relative to the vertical *Ṗ* axis is then seen to be very similar to the spacing of Delta, Gamma, and Eta Sagittae and the alignment of these stars with respect to the galactic equator. Delta and Gamma Sagittae are the stars that form the shaft of the Celestial Arrow, and Eta Sagittae is the target star toward which Sagitta is flying.

Converting $P-\dot{P}$ Coordinates into Galactic Coordinates

Using the P and $\dot{P}$ values that these pulsars had on May 1, 1992 (Table 3), we obtain the following relation:*

$$\ell° = 63.3687 + 5.1495 \times \log P$$
$$b° = 39.6429 + 3.4766 \times \log \dot{P}.$$

Now, by taking the P and $\dot{P}$ values for PSR 1930+22 from Table 3 and plugging them into the above equations, we can see how closely this "pulsar map" predicts the galactic longitude and latitude coordinates for the constellation star Eta Sagittae. Doing so, we get a map coordinate position of (59.04°, -6.39°) which deviates by only 0.2 degrees from Eta Sagittae's actual sky position of (59.18°, -6.23°). If we instead construct our pulsar map using the P and $\dot{P}$ values that the Crab and Vela pulsars had 23 years earlier in 1969, we find that the pulsar map predicts the same map coordinate position for Eta Sagittae even though the P and $\dot{P}$ values for the Crab and Vela pulsars have each changed considerably in the intervening time.

TABLE 3
Period and Period Derivatives for Three Unique Pulsars

Pulsar	Period (s)	Period Derivative (s/s)	Date
Crab	0.033403347	4.209599×10^{-13}	1 May 92
Vela	0.089298530	$1.258 \pm 0.008 \times 10^{-13}$	1 May 92
Vulpecula	0.144457105	5.75318×10^{-14}	1 May 92

---

* The values of the constants used to convert P and $\dot{P}$ into ℓ and b depend on the time unit used to measure the pulsar periods and on the base of the logarithm used. To produce the pulsar map, it is not important what measurement system we use provided that we use it consistently. In our calculations we adopt seconds for a time measure and base 10 for our logarithm operation, in accordance with figure 37. Also the conversion constants are based on the P and $\dot{P}$ values which the Crab and Vela pulsars had on Julian date 2,448,743 (May 1, 1992).

By identifying the $P-\dot{P}$ coordinates for the Crab and Vela pulsar with the present galactic longitude and latitude (ℓ, b) coordinates of Delta Sagittae and Gamma Sagittae, it is possible to derive a mathematical relation for converting $P-\dot{P}$ coordinates into galactic coordinates; see text box above.

The Vulpecula pulsar (PSR 1930+22) does not have anywhere near as many distinguishing features as the Crab and Vela pulsars. It is only of average radio brightness; it does not emit pulses in the optical, X-ray or gamma region of the spectrum; and its period does not exhibit glitches. Nevertheless, like the Crab pulsar, it is superimposed on a supernova remnant shell and is located near the 12,150 B.C. superwave event horizon, the ellipsoidal boundary that demarks the observed location of the superwave cosmic ray volley that passed the Earth 14,150 years ago (figure 31).[1,2] However, since the Vulpecula pulsar's background remnant is at least 300,000 years old, the supernova explosion that produced it could not have been triggered by this particular superwave.

The Vulpecula pulsar is also distinctive in that it is physically located just 0.13 degrees from the Galactic center's one-radian meridian, closer than any other pulsar. In this respect, it is very fitting that this pulsar should represent Eta Sagittae (η Sge) on the $P-\dot{P}$ map, since the Sagitta constellation pictures this as the star toward which the Arrow is flying. When the entire pulsar population is plotted, additional pulsar coordinate points crowd in near the Vela and Vulpecula pulsar $P-\dot{P}$ points, somewhat confusing the clarity of the "Sagitta map." However, the Crab, Vela, and Vulpecula pulsars are sufficiently unique as to stand out from the rest.

An Event Chronometer

As explained in chapter 4, the constellation of Sagitta (The Celestial Arrow) is a key part of the zodiac star lore cipher in that it uses the radian concept to convey the idea that a cosmic ray outburst, or superwave, traveled all the way from the Galactic center to our solar system, arriving on the date indicated by Sagittarius' arrow indicator. Knowing this, we are led to consider whether the pulsar map representation of Sagitta may be conveying a message about this recent Galactic superwave and whether it too may be an *event chronometer* similar to Sagittarius' arrow. Recall Sagittarius' arrow not only points out the location of the Galactic center but also serves as a chronometer that indicates the date when the most recent major superwave began passing the Earth (see chapter 4). That is, the Archer's aim gradually departs from his designated target, the Heart of the Scorpion, because the sky positions of the nearby stars forming the Archer's arrow (γ Sag and δ Sag) slowly change as these stars drift relative to distant background stars. However, when we regress the positions of these stars back in time, we find that the arrow would have been on target around 16,000 years ago, which gives the date when a Galactic center outburst would have first become apparent to Earth observers.[3]

The Vela pulsar coordinate point, which represents the head of the pulsar map "arrow" is drifting to the right in the $P-\dot{P}$ map due to the gradual lengthening of Vela's period at the rate of 1.25×10^{-13} seconds per second. So, it is natural to instead look to the past and ask: *on what past date would the Vela pulsar have had a pulsation period equal to the present period of the Crab pulsar?* Knowing that the Vela pulsar is currently pulsing about 2.67 times slower than the Crab pulsar (11.2 pulses per second as compared with 29.8 pulses per second). and knowing the rate at which the Vela pulsar is slowing down, through a simple calculation we find that Vela would have had the Crab pulsar's present pulsation rate about $14,100 \pm 100$ years ago.[*] Interestingly, the superwave that triggered the Vela and Crab Nebula supernova explosions would have been passing Earth on this designated date.

As noted earlier, polar ice core data indicates that galactic cosmic ray intensity outside the solar system had reached a peak around $14,150 \pm 150$ years ago and had begun its rise to that climax some centuries earlier perhaps around $14,300 \pm 200$ years ago. Noting that this peak was one of the most prominent of the last ice age, the possibility suggests itself that the Vela and Crab pulsars are highly accurate chronometers of ETI origin that have been placed in space to inform us about this key superwave date.

The geologic record registers a number of other things happening around the time of this superwave passage.[4] The Earth's climate began to warm up very rapidly beginning about 12,700 B.C. and reached a temperature peak around this 12,150 year B.C. date, this period of unusual ice age warmth being known as the Bölling Interstadial. This warming could have been initiated by cosmic dust and gas that the superwave brought into the solar system, which in turn increased the Sun's activity and also increased the amount of solar radiation that the Earth received through scattered light. Other data indicate that at this time the glacial ice sheets were melting at their fastest rate and causing widespread continental flooding. This date also marked the beginning of a major episode of mammal extinction that climaxed 1500 years later most likely as a result of a

---

[*] This time span calculation presumes that the Vela pulsar's rate of period change ($\dot{P}$) does not change over time. Although its value does decrease with time, it rapidly resets back to a higher value when a pulsar glitch occurs. Due to the irregularity of this glitch-reset phenomenon, more data must be collected before we can determine whether the average $\dot{P}$ in fact changes over the long-term.

solar flare cosmic ray disaster. In addition, around 12,200 B.C. the Earth's north magnetic pole abruptly flipped southward for a period of several decades, possibly caused by the impact of intense solar flare outbursts from an excessively energized Sun.

It is quite fitting that the Crab, Vela, and Vulpecula pulsars, which mark sites where major celestial explosions once took place, would be used to transmit a picture of Sagitta, a constellation that in our star lore symbolizes the passage of a catastrophic core explosion superwave.[5] Moreover to the extent that a supernova causes the death of a star, pulsars associated with them might be viewed as warning beacons. It is also appropriate that ETI civilizations would utilize communication beacons that use cosmic ray beams to emit synchrotron radiation, the same type of radiation that is emitted from superwave cosmic rays.

A Celestial Memorial to a Terrestrial Cataclysm

Probably one of the most perplexing discoveries is that the entire Crab supernova remnant itself appears to be an immense three-dimensional celestial map that accurately depicts the present contour of the 12,150 B.C. superwave wavefront. Compare the shape of the nebula shown in figure 30 with the oval event horizon shown in figure 31. Like the superwave event horizon, the Crab Nebula has the shape of a prolate ellipsoid, one that is elongated like an American football rather than squashed like a flying saucer. Moreover the nebula's major and minor axes happen to have about the same length ratio as the major and minor axes of the superwave event horizon ellipsoid. Measuring about 13.8 by 10.6 light years in extent, the Crab Nebula has an axial ratio of 1.30, very close to the 1.295 axial ratio that the 12,150 B.C. superwave event horizon would have had in 1054 AD when the Crab supernova explosion became visible.* Currently, the event horizon has an axial ratio of 1.27. So, the Crab Nebula approximates a 1:4500 scale model of the shape that the superwave event horizon would have had in 1054 AD.

---

* The major-to-minor axis ratio of this event horizon progressively decreases with the increase in time that has elapsed since its Earth passage date. More specifically this ratio is given as $(23 + t)/(46t + t^2)^{1/2}$, where t is the time in thousands of years since the date of superwave passage. This assumes that the Galactic center lies 23,000 light years away (~7.1 kiloparsecs). If the Galactic center distance is instead figured to be as great as 26,000 light years, this ratio would calculate to be 1.34 in 1054 AD and 1.31 at present.

The Crab Nebula:
Scale Model of the Superwave Event Horizon

The Crab supernova remnant shell serves as a scale model of the 12,150 B.C. superwave event horizon for the following reasons:

- It has a prolate spheroid shape, like the event horizon.

- It has the same 1.30 axial ratio that the event horizon would have had on the date of the Crab supernova.

- The nebula's minor axis has the same orientation as the event horizon minor axis. The nebula's major axis is rotated by 90 degrees to the event horizon major axis, making it broadside to our viewing direction.

- Like the superwave event horizon, it emits synchrotron radiation. The cosmic rays producing this radiation are most likely supplied by this outward traveling superwave.

Furthermore, the nebula's long axis is oriented parallel to the galactic plane and perpendicular to the Galactic center – anticenter axis. In other words, this ellipsoid "scale model map" is rotated so that its major axis is oriented almost exactly perpendicular to the major axis of the superwave event horizon. Just a coincidence? Since our line of sight toward the Crab Nebula is aligned with the Galactic center–anticenter axis, the nebula is also aligned perpendicular to our viewing direction, making its unique elliptical shape *most apparent from our observing location*.

Since the Crab remnant consists of material ejected from a central explosion, it serves as an appropriate symbolic representation of the Galactic superwave whose cosmic rays were similarly explosively ejected. Moreover the cosmic ray electrons trapped within the Crab Nebula's ellipsoidal shell radiate a synchrotron radiation continuum much like those journeying outward at the superwave event horizon. From our location within the superwave shell, we observe this superwave radio emission as the diffuse background radiation which astronomers have termed the Galactic radio background radiation.

In addition, as we have already mentioned, the Crab, Vela, and Millisecond pulsars share certain similarities, that occur very rarely among pulsars, and which encourage us to conceptually interrelate these three pulsars. The one-radian symbolism of the Millisecond Pulsar, combined with the Crab and Vela pulsar $P-\dot{P}$ mapping of the Sagitta arrow constellation with its 12,100 year B.C. date evoke the idea of the superwave event horizon's radial light-speed flight away from the Galactic center, a phenomenon that is further corroborated by the dates for the Crab and Vela supernova explosions. All of this symbolism together reinforces the idea that the Crab Nebula forms a map of the 12,150 B.C. superwave event horizon.

These similarities of the shape and orientation of the Crab Nebula to that of the superwave event horizon may just be a series of unusual happenstances of nature, or perhaps they could indicate that the Crab supernova was intentionally engineered, a cosmic fireworks display performed for the benefit of civilizations in our Galactic sector. The second conclusion balks the imagination. To induce a stellar supernova and to then shape the resulting explosion, these cosmic artisans would necessarily have mastered the ability to manipulate nature's energy processes on an inconceivably grand scale.

In addition, the Crab supernova occurred in a unique location relative to the solar system. As mentioned before, of all young supernova remnants (those less than 2000 years old), the Crab Nebula is the closest one to our solar neighborhood and also is the closest to the Galactic *anticenter* (figure 28). Recall that the Galactic anticenter is the direction in the sky that lies directly opposite to the Galactic center. Hence the anticenter direction relative to background stars will depend on the viewer's location in the galactic disk. When considered in view of the Crab Nebula's unusual brightness, its unique ellipsoidal shape, and its careful orientation parallel to the galactic plane and perpendicular to our line of sight, it becomes difficult to imagine that all this was just purely accidental.

Also the Crab Nebula is uniquely situated relative to key constellation stars. It is located in the Taurus constellation very close to the line that extends between the two stars marking the tips of Taurus' horns, and lies slightly more than one degree from Taurus' southern horn tip (figure 38). As I have shown in *Earth Under Fire*, the charging Celestial Bull in ancient Egyptian myth and Minoan custom signified the Galactic catastrophe that long ago brought havoc to the Earth.[6] Taurus, who is shown charging toward the Galactic anticenter, symbolizes the superwave as it advances away from the Galactic center and the tips of his horns signify the superwave's forefront. Orion, who confronts the Bull with raised shield and points out the Galactic anticenter with his club, is by

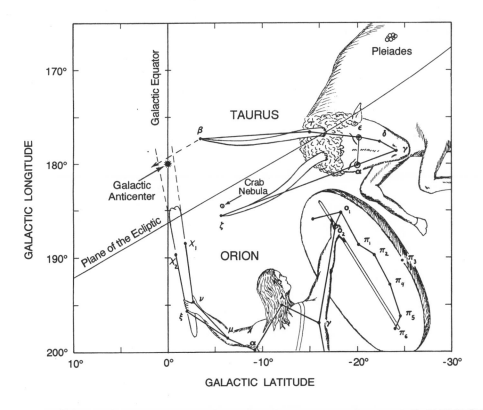

Figure 38. A map showing the constellations of Taurus and Orion with the position of the Crab Nebula marked out near the tip of the Taurus' lower horn (LaViolette, *Earth Under Fire*, figure 3.3).

tradition a memorial set in the sky to honor those who died in this global catastrophe. It is very interesting that the Crab Nebula is so appropriately placed in this symbolic reenactment of humanity's encounter with the Galactic superwave. Just as the nebula is situated at the forefront of the charging Bull, so too the nebula is presently being impacted by cosmic rays traveling at the forefront of the superwave.

In addition, the Crab Nebula is distinguished as being the only Galactic supernova remnant to lie so close to the Earth's ecliptic plane. The Crab pulsar is positioned just 1.314 degrees below the ecliptic. The pulsar's close proximity to pulsar PSR 0525+21 also draws attention to the nebula's ecliptic position. As noted in the previous chapter, these two pulsars are not only unusually close to one another, but they also share the rare phenomenon of pulse glitching. Among the subset of known glitching pulsars, the Crab pulsar has the shortest period and PSR 0525+21 has the longest period. Since it would be extremely unusual to find two glitching pulsars so close together, less than one chance in 10^{127}, it is natural to examine their positional relation relative to one another.

What we find is quite remarkable. A line connecting these two pulsars comes within a few degrees of being parallel to Earth's ecliptic plane (figure 36) and currently *deviates by 0.008 degrees from being exactly parallel to the 2000 AD celestial equator* (will be exact in 2060 AD). Moreover the two pulsars are presently separated from one another by $1.3144 \pm 0.0012°$ of arc, which *equals the Crab pulsar's present 1.3140° latitudinal deviation from the ecliptic plane, to within the millidegree accuracy of knowing the positions of these pulsars*! Could PSR 0525+21 have been purposely positioned near the Crab pulsar to call attention to the Crab supernova remnant's position relative to our ecliptic plane?

These unusual positional arrangements compel us to consider whether the Crab Nebula supernova explosion is purposely being marked for our viewing benefit and not merely for civilizations in our general Galactic locale. If so, is humanity considered so important that this Galactic community would go to these grand efforts to produce this immense nebula map specifically for us?

The location of the Crab Nebula may be personalizing its message for us in yet another way. The distance from the Earth to the Crab Nebula, which is measured to be 6585 ± 30 light-years, also designates a light travel time period that amounts to about one fourth of the time taken for the Earth's precessing poles to complete one circuit of the ecliptic, a full polar "Great Cycle" taking approximately 26,000 years. Interestingly, the time required for the 12,130 B.C. superwave event horizon to travel the Galactic center radial distance from our solar system to the Crab Nebula's progenitor star, a total of 6520 years, when added to 6585 years, the time required for light from the Crab supernova explosion to travel the intervening distance back to us, yields a round-trip travel time of $13,105 \pm 60$ years. By comparison, in 12,130 B.C., when that supernova-triggering event horizon was passing the solar system, the time required for the Earth's pole to precess 180 degrees, half of a Great Cycle period, averaged 13,070 years.

If this explosion was purposefully arranged, it suggests that its perpetrators not only knew the plane of Earth's orbit around the Sun, but also the rate at which the Earth's poles precess. Taken out of context, the idea of an intelligently sited supernova would sound absurd. But viewed in terms of the other "coincidences" noted earlier, it may be a thought worth considering.

Let us further investigate the Crab Nebula's position along the ecliptic from the standpoint of whether it might represent an intentional time marker. That is, the Earth's poles precess along the ecliptic at a very regular rate, and this gradual polar movement causes the seasons to change relative to the background constellations. By noting the position of the moving vernal equinox relative to stationary markers such as the boundaries between zodiac constellations, ancient cultures were able to designate the passage of zodiacal ages and the dates of significant events that took place thousands of years past. In a similar fashion, a Galactic community may have intentionally detonated the Crab supernova to mark a particular date on the Great Cycle chronometer.

As shown above, the Crab Nebula's singular location appears to implicate a kind of purposeful arrangement, as though these sky artisans carefully selected the location of the supernova progenitor star in order to convey to us that they knew the location of our ecliptic plane and the rate at which our planet's poles have been precessing. If so, might they also have chosen this particular location because its longitudinal position along the ecliptic might call our attention to a particular date in the past? If we regard the vernal equinox as the Great Cycle time indicator, as is traditional practice, we find that it would have been positioned at the Crab Nebula's ecliptic longitude in the year 4,277 ± 25 B.C. This date is not very significant from an astronomical or geological standpoint other than being 1250 years after the actual date of the Crab supernova. Although, interestingly, it does fall within 40 years of 4240 B.C., the zero date for the ancient Egyptian Sothic calendar.*[7]

---

* The Egyptians had two calendars. Their Sothic calendar, which was based on the heliacal rising of the star Sirius, accurately measured out the year as 365 days. Their "vague year" calendar measured out the year instead as a whole number of 365 days. As a result of this discrepancy, the two calendars would begin on the same day only once every 1460 years. On that day of calendric coincidence, the Egyptians would celebrate their New Year at their sacred Temple of Hathor at Dendereh, the first such New Year being on 4240 B.C., the beginning of the Sothic calendar. Interestingly, the zodiac found on the ceiling of this temple displays among its constellations a New Year date marker figured as a cow with a star between its horns. The cow symbolized Hathor, the cow headed goddess, a form of Isis, and the star presumably denoted her star Sothis (Sirius). We can only wonder about their foresight to depict a cow with a star between its horns as their New Year marker,

If we instead consider the date that comes one quarter of a precessional cycle earlier when the winter solstice coincided with the Crab Nebula marker, we arrive at a more meaningful date of 10,782 ± 50 B.C. This correlates with the climax of the terminal Pleistocene extinction (10,750 ± 100 B.C.), the most significant large animal mass extinction episode to occur since the demise of the dinosaurs. Both geologic evidence and legend indicate that, at the time of this catastrophe, the Earth endured a period of extreme heat which caused vast deluges of glacial meltwater to sweep over the continents. One theory suggests that this conflagration occurred when the Earth became engulfed by a hazardous solar coronal mass ejection.[8] The associated barrage of solar flare cosmic ray particles would account for the instability of the Earth's magnetic field during this period as well as for the high levels of atmospheric radiocarbon and 50 fold higher solar cosmic ray intensity recorded in moon rocks. The Sun appears to have been aggravated into this active state by cosmic dust and gas injected into the solar system by a passing superwave, the same superwave that is currently energizing the Crab Nebula.

At the time of this mass extinction, the vernal equinox was positioned at the boundary between the constellations of Virgo and Leo, designated by the boundary stars Omega Virginis and Beta Leonis. Our ancestors attached such great importance to this episode that they memorialized its time of occurrence by using star constellations to reference this vernal equinox position. For example, the ancient Egyptians and ancient Greeks both chose this ecliptic boundary as the starting point for their precessional Great Cycle calendar. Also, one ancient Greek flood myth records this date by describing how Zeus punished mankind with a deluge immediately after the goddess of harvest, Astraea, had departed from Earth. Since she was represented by the Virgo constellation, her departure refers to the time when the Age of Virgo had ended and the vernal equinox was about to pass into Leo.[9] Remembrance of this Virgo-Leo boundary date has also been preserved in the floor mosaic found in the sixth century AD Beth Alpha Synagogue. This depicts a zodiac with the spring equinox positioned at the Virgo-Leo boundary. The center of the mosaic displays the sun god Helios with his four steeds, calling to mind the ancient Greek conflagration

---

the first New Year falling near the date indicated by the Crab supernova ecliptic marker, a supernova that occurred between the horns of Taurus.

myth about Phaethon and the sun chariot.

So, the Crab Nebula, through its unique sky position, located near the tip of Taurus' southern horn, may be memorializing one of the worst mass extinction episodes to occur in recent geologic history and which, according to legend, involved the loss of many human lives. But the Crab Nebula also contains a very unique pulsar that is part of the phenomenal interstellar superwave message we have been analyzing. So, if pulsars have been created by a network of Galactic civilizations, it seems that these civilizations may have been well acquainted with the solar flare cataclysm that affected our planet at the time of the last superwave passage.

A Superwave Shield?

One of the most perplexing features of the Crab supernova remnant is the tubular jet of ionized gas that is seen jutting outward from its northern side (figure 39). This immense tube extends about 2½ light years beyond the perimeter of the nebula and has a diameter measuring roughly 1½ light years. Its unusually straight and parallel sides contrast remarkably with the irregularly twisted filaments that make up the rest of the nebula.

In their 1982 *Astrophysical Journal* article reporting on this "mysterious jet" astronomers Theodore Gull and Robert Fesen raised the following perplexing questions:

> First, why is the jet the only filamentary extension outside an otherwise well-bounded nebula, and second, why does it have such an organized structure in a largely chaotic and amorphous-appearing supernova remnant? Because of its appearance, it is not clear that the jet has undergone the same physical processes which shaped the rest of the nebula. Though its structure suggests an energetic origin, it is not obvious that the jet is directly related to the AD 1054 supernova event since it is not in radial alignment with either the center of expansion or the pulsar. . . clearly more information regarding the jet's physical properties. . . is required before one can realistically attempt to understand the jet's structure and origin.[10]

Moreover observations of material in the jet's northern tip show it to be receding from us at a relatively low velocity of 100 to 150 kilometers per second which contrasts with the high velocity of the nebula's outer envelope which expands at rates ranging from 1500 to 2200 kilometers per second. As a result, astronomers have concluded that the jet must be oriented nearly in the plane of the sky, with most of its material moving perpendicular to our line of sight.[11]

Figure 39. The Crab Nebula and its optical jet imaged with special green and red filters that pass light emitted from doubly ionized oxygen as well as from ionized hydrogen and nitrogen. Right image shows a magnified view. (Gull and Fesen, *Astrophysical Journal*, figures 2b, 2c).

But long-term observation of 14 luminous filaments in the jet shows that this material is moving directly away from the nebula's center of expansion, like the filaments in other parts of the nebula, and not in the direction of the jet's long axis. This has perplexed astronomers who were expecting to find a reasonable way to explain the jet, since their observations indicate that it cannot have been formed by the nebula's explosion. Astronomers Robert Fesen and Bryan Staker comment about this as follows in their 1993 *Monthly Notices* paper:

> ...the expansion directions of the 14 measured jet features appear most consistent with a simple radial expansion directed away from the centre of the remnant... It seems, therefore, that all image data available to us point to a radial-like expansion, in direct contradiction to the expected non-radial motions which the optical structure of the jet seems to demand... If correct, it means that the parallel-edged jet structure is not the result of peculiar non-radial kinematics along the northern boundary of the Crab.[12]

As we see, astronomers are thoroughly perplexed as to why the jet is not aligned with the nebula's expansion center for, if it was, its formation might be explained by the natural process of nebular expansion. Nevertheless, such off-center alignment is precisely the kind of thing that an ETI civilization would do to ensure that the

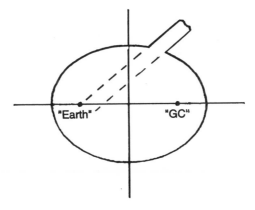

Figure 40. A sketch showing the location of the foci of the Crab Nebula's ellipsoid and the relative orientation of its optical jet.

recipients of their message did not mistake it for a natural phenomenon, and as we see, the Crab Nebula jet certainly did get the perplexed attention of our astronomers.

However, if we look carefully at the orientation of the jet, which makes approximately a 40° angle to the nebula's major axis, we see that it may be purposefully positioned. Its eastern edge (left side in the photo) *is aimed directly at the southern focus of the nebula's ellipsoid* (see figure 40). There is no natural explanation for such an alignment since explosion ejecta would always scatter outward from the explosion center point, not from one of the foci of the ellipsoid that the explosion happened to form.

It is not clear whether this siting is relevant in the context of the scale model Crab Nebula map discussed earlier. Recall that the two foci of the ellipsoid would represent respectively the Galactic center and the Earth. So if the southern ellipsoid focus is interpreted as representing the Earth, the map would then be showing the jet as symbolically aiming toward the Earth.

If the Crab supernova explosion was purposely engineered by a highly advanced extraterrestrial civilization, then such an unusual organized feature does not come as such a surprise. But the question that naturally arises is how did they form this. Could the jet be an example of a cylindrical force field shield deployed to intercept superwave cosmic rays? Radio telescope studies show that the jet indeed emits polarized synchrotron radiation, which indicates that it is being energized by trapped cosmic rays (see radio jet in figure 30).[13] Could the civilization that engineered the Crab supernova remnant and its unique pulsar beacon also be demonstrating for our benefit a technology that might one day protect us from the onslaught of the next superwave? Note that the Crab Nebula map shows this jet or "shield" symbolically intervening between the Earth and the Galactic center. Perhaps these sky artisans are trying to tell us that we should be prepared to produce such a shield to shelter ourselves from the Galactic center.

This same shield metaphor has been left for us in our constellation lore. As seen in figure 38, Orion holds up a shield to ward off the Bull of Heaven (the Galactic superwave) which arrives from the Galactic center and charges toward the Galactic anticenter. We find the shield symbol also appearing in the constellation of Centaurus. As mentioned earlier, the one radian metaphor of the Sagitta and Crucis constellations (figure 20), leads us to symbolically "fold" the galactic coordinate map about its Galactic center longitude meridian so that both of these constellations approach our solar vicinity and coincide with one another, the distance from the Galactic center to the solar system being equal to the length of a one radian arc. We may then picture Centaurus facing the Galactic center and, with his upraised shield, sheltering our solar system from the Galactic superwave cosmic ray onslaught represented by the outward flying arrow Sagitta. In chapter 8 we will investigate the feasibility of deploying a force field technology that might form an effective space shield.

Cosmic Synchronicity?

For members of the Galactic ETI community to make such a major effort to create the Crab Nebula celestial map for our viewing, they must have known that our planet was inhabited. Let us suppose that these artisans resided not far from the Crab Nebula and learned about our planet by exchanging faster-than-light messages with other members of their Galactic "club" who lived in our solar neighborhood. Or, perhaps they made superluminal space travel expeditions to our planet, if such were possible. If our suspicions are correct, they may even have known something of our geological history, such as the occurrence of the 10,750 B.C. cataclysm which, legend tells us, brought a formerly flourishing global civilization to an abrupt end.

Yet one thing remains puzzling about the Crab Nebula ETI hypothesis and this concerns the thousands of years involved between the creation of this celestial map and the time when its message could be seen by Earth observers. The Crab Nebula is located about 6,585 light years away from us. So, in real time this supernova explosion would have occurred around 5530 B.C. and only some 6,585 years later, in 1054 AD, would it have become visible on Earth. But, in 5530 B.C. humanity was still in the Neolithic stone age period. The Old Kingdom of ancient Egypt did not emerge until around 3100 B.C. Supposing that the Galactic community had been informed of humanity's relatively low level of advancement in that era, how could they be sure that 7500 years later humans would have progressed to the point where they had the technological means to study the Crab Nebula and its pulsar? Large optical telescopes and radio telescopes are a prerequisite if the Crab Nebula's unique features are to be adequately discerned. Moreover a sophisticated knowledge of both Galactic and extragalactic astronomy is needed to understand the Crab Nebula's superwave warning message. The Crab Nebula sky map has been ready for us to study for at least the past 600 years, maybe even for the past 900 years. So, there are some centuries of leeway as to the time when the prerequisite science and technology infrastructure would finally be developed and its message finally understood.

But if this is an intentional message sent from the past, its crafters would need to have astounding precognitive abilities. In U.S. government research experiments, trained remote viewers have demonstrated up to 80 percent accuracy in viewing distant events taking place even thousands of miles away.[14] The same technique has been used to determine events that might occur in the future. Did alien clairvoyants remotely view our planet as it would be 7500 years in the future? Or, perhaps they knew that, given the size of the human population and its rate of growth, the number of people would have grown sufficiently large to have spawned a civilization of adequate technological advancement some seven millennia later.

One other possibility that presents itself is that members of this Galactic ETI network have been directly controlling the evolution of human society, thereby ensuring that we would be sufficiently advanced when their pulsar message was ready for viewing. Egyptologists have marveled at the sophisticated level of mathematics, science, engineering, and medicine that seemingly sprang out of nowhere at the dawn of civilization in ancient Egypt, much of which was progressively lost or forgotten over subsequent millennia.[15] Egyptian myth relates that the gods Osiris and Thoth

(Hermes Trismegistus) had visited their land and taught humanity the arts of civilization and the Hermetic knowledge. Some authors have interpreted this literally as evidence of ETI contact.

One other alternative that might be considered is that these civilizations simply chose this particular time because they knew in advance that another superwave was due to pass through our part of the Galaxy around this time. Their efforts to warn us about the phenomenon at this time may have been intended as a precautionary measure in case we had not figured things out on our own.

The Eclipsing Binary Millisecond (EBM) Pulsar exhibits a "coincidental" correspondence with the Vela pulsar period that is obvious only if their signals are observed during the past several decades. Namely, the signal timing from the EBM pulsar shows a sinusoidal variation of ±0.089226 seconds over the course of its 9.2 hour orbital cycle. This corresponds to the time taken for the pulsar's radio signals to transit the 26,770 kilometer radius of the EBM Pulsar's *highly circular* orbit.[*16] This signal timing variation happens to very closely match the pulsation period of the Vela pulsar, the discrepancy presently being only 0.09 percent! In fact, Vela's period had precisely this 0.089226 second value in September of 1973 and has since been diverging from it by about 0.004 percent per year due to the gradual slowing of its pulsation rate. One thousand years before or after this date Vela's period would depart from this orbital radius value by 4 percent, and the association would not be as obvious.

If these pulsars are entirely of natural origin, then we must consider it a simple stroke of luck that we are observing them at this unique point in time, during their many thousands of years of existence, when they would show this correspondence. If instead they are of ETI origin, their periods being carefully chosen to convey an association between the EBM Pulsar and the Vela pulsar, then some degree of foresight was necessary. Since the Vela pulsar, the nearer of the two, is located about 800 light years from us, an alien civilization would have had to plan in advance at least 800 years for this period coincidence to be occurring at present.

The possibility that the EBM/Vela pulsar synchronicity was

---

* As the pulsar cycles further from us and nearer to us, its pulsed signal alternately retards and advances by ±0.089226 seconds from the value it would normally have if it remained stationary. This interval of 0.089226 seconds represents the time required for the pulsar's radio signal to traverse the radius of its orbit about its companion star.

intentional becomes more plausible when we realize that it fits with other parts of the metaphorical pulsar message we have been analyzing. As we saw in chapter 3, the EBM Pulsar is the closest pulsar to Gamma Sagittae, which suggests an associative link with this one-radian indicator star. Also as we saw earlier, the $P-\dot{P}$ constellation map makes sense if we interpret the Vela pulsar coordinate as representing the star Gamma Sagittae. So since both the EBM and Vela pulsars are associated in common with Gamma Sagittae, a symbolic association between these two pulsars seems appropriate.

Moreover by "encoding" the Vela pulsar period as the *radius* of the EBM Pulsar's highly circular orbit, the association of these two pulsars appears to be combined with the one-radian concept. That is, the 0.089226 light-second radial distance subtends an angle of one radian when laid out along the EBM Pulsar's nearly perfectly circular orbital circumference. The EBM Pulsar also portrays the one-radian concept in connection with Gamma Sagittae. As we saw earlier, this pulsar is so positioned in the sky as to form a right angle with Gamma Sagittae and with the Galaxy's nearby equatorial one-radian point (figure 18).

Together, these allusions emphasize the idea of interpreting both Gamma Sagittae and the Vela pulsar as indicating a one-radian arrow flight from the Galactic center to the solar environs (see also the text box below).

Is the Degree a Galactic Standard of Angular Measurement?

Dividing the orbital radius of the EBM Pulsar (0.0892262 light-seconds) by the period of the Millisecond Pulsar (0.0015578 seconds) yields the ratio 57.277, a number that is within three hundredths of a percent of the number of degrees in one radian (57.296). In this indirect fashion, these two pulsars could be expressing the one radian concept. Also if we take the period of the Vela pulsar and divide by the period of the Millisecond Pulsar, we find that this period ratio was exactly equal to the number of degrees in one radian in April of 1981 and has since been deviating from this value by 0.004% per year due to the gradual increase of the Vela pulsar's period. We cannot be certain that a Galactic commune of intercommunicating civilizations would be using a system of angular measurement that subdivides a circle into 360 degrees. Nevertheless it is interesting to find that the period ratio of these two unique pulsars equals the number of degrees in one radian.

Chapter 7

Natural or Artificial

Lighthouse Trouble

Supernova Origin Problem. Although astronomers continue to use the neutron star lighthouse model to interpret the pulsar phenomenon, they readily admit that there are many things that this model leaves unexplained. One shortcoming is that it fails to explain how pulsars originate. The lighthouse model predicts they should be formed in supernova explosions. However, little evidence has been found of pulsars residing within or near existing supernova remnants. Although several pulsars have been found to coincide with remnants, a supernova cause remains uncertain, even for these few. In the case of the Vela, Crab, and Vulpecula pulsars, the evidence contradicts the idea that they were formed by the explosion that produced their associated remnants. As was noted in chapter 5, the trajectory of the Vela pulsar is not aligned with the explosion center of the Vela supernova remnant. Neither could it have covered the distance from that site to its present location in the 13,000 years since the time of the Vela supernova explosion. Also it is not certain that the Vela pulsar is located at the same distance as the Vela supernova remnant. By noting the frequency-dependent time lag of its radio signals, astronomers had estimated that the pulsar should lie about 1650 light years away. But this is twice as far away as the estimated distance to the Vela remnant.

The Crab pulsar also poses a problem. When its trajectory is regressed to the time of the supernova, its location misses the explosion site by about a third of a light year — 20,000 times the distance from the Earth to the Sun. Also unlike the debris that composes the expanding nebula, the pulsar is not traveling away from the explosion center but rather is heading off *at a tangent* to the trajectory of nebular expansion. Astronomers concur that a causal connection between the Vulpecula pulsar and its remnant is doubtful as well because, judging from its large size, the remnant appears to be too old.

Circular Orbit Problem. Pulsar astronomers have been surprised to find that a large percentage of pulsars are associated with an orbiting companion. For if pulsars are formed in supernova explosions, as their theory predicts, any nearby celestial bodies should have become propelled far from the explosion site and from the newly formed neutron star. For this reason, astronomers assume that a pulsar acquires its companions *after* the explosion through gravitational capture of closely passing bodies. In such a case, the captured planets or stars should have highly elliptical orbits much like short period comets orbiting the Sun. But contrary to this expectation most binary pulsars are orbited by bodies that follow exceedingly circular orbits. One example is pulsar PSR 1257+12 which is found to be associated with two planets, each about 3 to 4 times the mass of the Earth, which follow highly circular orbits around the pulsar.[1] Another pulsar, PSR 0329+54, is orbited by a companion having an even lower mass, somewhere between 6 and 57 percent of the Earth's mass.[2] Again, the data indicate that its orbit is quite circular, posing serious problems for a supernova origin.

PSR 1957+20, the Eclipsing Binary Millisecond (EBM) Pulsar, also presents problems for the standard neutron star theory. Its companion is estimated to be a white dwarf with a mass equal to about 2 percent of the Sun's mass. Although this is considerably more massive than a planet, even a body this massive could not have survived the expulsive force of a supernova explosion. Pulsar timing indicates that this companion's orbit has an eccentricity of less than 40 parts per million, indicating that its orbit deviates from perfect circularity by less than one part per billion.[3] Compared with the Earth's orbit, this one is five thousand times more precisely circular. The circularity of its orbit precludes the possibility that the pulsar had gravitationally captured its white dwarf companion after the explosion. It is also unlikely that its companion spontaneously grew from material orbiting the pulsar since all current neutron star theories suggest that the pulsar is eroding its companion, not contributing to its growth. The body orbiting another pulsar, PSR J2317+1439, exhibits an even smaller orbital eccentricity of just 0.5 parts per million!

Orbits so *nearly perfect* in circularity are a rarity in astronomy. We find them only in connection with pulsars. Since no adequate explanation is forthcoming from theories proposing that pulsars originate in supernova explosions, this raises the question as to whether pulsars and their orbits may be one more aspect of ETI engineering. If pulsars have masses comparable to that of the Sun, as astronomical measurements seem to indicate, their creators, then would have to possess technologies far beyond what we know in order to enable them to engineer bodies of such enormous mass. Those wishing to stick with the theory that pulsars are natural objects such as spinning neutron stars, must posit the repeated occurrence of a miracle of nature to explain these findings. In that case, a viable possibility is that we are just beginning to discover that nature is itself intelligent.

Multiple Pulse Problem. The lighthouse model also has diffi-culty accounting for pulse profiles that are composed of two pulses: a main pulse and an interpulse. In order for two pulses to be seen per cycle, the neutron star would have to emit two beams of synchrotron radiation, one from each of its magnetic poles and the magnetic pole axis would have to be oriented nearly perpendicular to the neutron star's spin axis. Then, as the star rotated, an observer aligned with its equatorial plane would see pulses alternately coming from each radiation beam. In cases where the cosmic ray beams were not oriented close to the star's equator, the lighthouse model predicts that viewers should instead see only a single pulse with each rotation.

However, this model has been unable to explain the pulses coming from the Crab Nebula pulsar. In this case, the interpulse follows the main pulse by 40 percent of a cycle, rather than by half of a cycle, as the dual-beam lighthouse model would predict (see figure 41). To produce such a pulse pattern the pulsar's magnetic poles would have to be bent at an angle of about 145° with respect to one another instead of directly opposing one another, as would normally be expected for the magnetic field of a celestial body.

The Crab pulsar is one of the few pulsars that emits pulses at the high energy end of the electromagnetic spectrum. As mentioned earlier, besides radio pulses, it produces flashes of visible light, X-rays, and gamma rays. But the lighthouse model runs into trouble when it attempts to explain how pulses in these diverse portions of the spectrum might be generated from the same set of neutron star electron beams. Although the pulse profiles in all these spectral regions are synchronized with one another, in other respects they are substantially different. For example, the radio pulse profile is much narrower than the optical, X-ray, and gamma ray profiles (figure 41). Also the pulsar's signal intensity is found to drop off with increasing frequency at differing rates in each of these energy

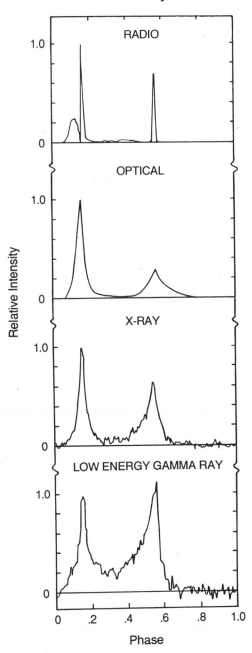

Figure 41. Time-averaged pulse profile for the Crab Nebula pulsar, as seen at radio, optical, X-ray, and gamma ray wavelengths (after Wilson & Fishman, *Astrophysical Journal*, figure 4; Taylor & Manchester, *Annual Reviews Astronomy & Astrophysics*, figure 4).

ranges, indicating that the radio, optical, X-ray and gamma ray pulses are produced by different cosmic ray sources. This poses a serious problem for the standard lighthouse model which hypothe-sizes a single beam of cosmic ray electrons coming from each magnetic pole.

Another feature that poses difficulty for the Crab pulsar lighthouse model is that the number of pulse components changes radically depending on which portion of the radio spectrum the pulsar is observed at. For example, between frequencies of about 430 to 606 megahertz a small precursor pulse is found to immediately precede the main radio pulse whereas at other radio frequencies, and also at optical, X-ray, and gamma ray wavelengths, only a single main pulse component is present. Moreover, the Crab pulsar's interpulse is present throughout the electromagnetic spectrum, from radio to gamma ray frequencies, but is *mysteriously absent* in the 2,700 megahertz frequency range. To further complicate matters, at progressively higher radio frequencies in the 4,700 to 8,400 mega-hertz range, the interpulse returns *but is now shifted to an earlier phase,* now arriving 0.9 milliseconds (2.8% of a pulse period) ahead of its previous position. *Moreover the interpulse is now followed by two new peaks that did not show up in any other frequency range,* yielding a total of four peaks at 4,700 megahertz. But at 8,400 megahertz, *the main pulse peak entirely disappears,* leaving just the interpulse and the two additional peaks.

All of these peculiarities present enormous problems for scientists attempting to account for the Crab pulsar emission in terms of a natural phenomenon. Astronomers David Moffett and Timothy Hankins comment about this finding as follows:

> In a multifrequency study of the Crab pulsar, we have found new and unusual components that defy explanation by emission from a simple dipole field geometry.[4]

The lighthouse model is confronted with an equally puzzling situation when attempting to explain the emission from the Vela pulsar. Like the Crab pulsar, Vela emits two pulses per cycle in the optical and gamma ray spectral regions. However, throughout the radio spectral region, it produces just one pulse per cycle (see figure 42). Moreover Vela's radio, optical, X-ray, and gamma ray pulses are not synchronized with one another. At gamma ray frequencies, its main pulse and interpulse are separated by 42 percent of a cycle, whereas at optical and X-ray frequencies they are separated by just 23 percent of a cycle. Its single radio frequency peak is also out of

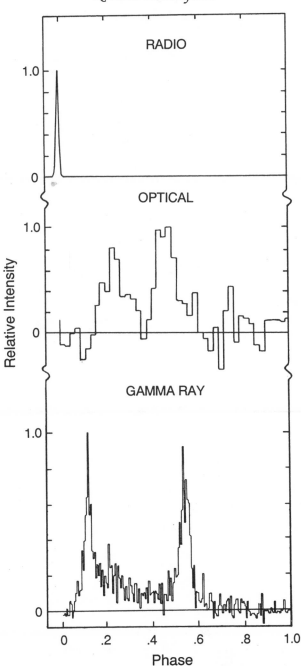

Figure 42. Time-averaged pulse profile for the Vela pulsar, as seen at radio, optical, and gamma ray wavelengths (after Kanbach, *Astronomy and Astrophysics*, figures 1 and 2).

phase with all of these higher energy peaks. So, as with the Crab pulsar, the dual-beam lighthouse model fails to account for the Vela pulsar's complex emission. Some theorists have been tempted to postulate three pairs of magnetic poles projecting particle beams from various points on the star's surface, but in the realm of natural phenomena this begins to approach the boundaries of the unbelievable. Models that attempt to explain the Crab pulsar's behavior fail to account for Vela's totally different pulsation characteristics.

Spin Axis Orientation Paradox. Pulsars that combine a wide pulse profile with a dual pulse signal (main pulse plus interpulse) present a serious problem for the lighthouse model. For example, the Crab pulsar's pulses span 60 to 70 percent of its cycle. Vela's optical, X-ray, and gamma ray pulses span 70 to 80 percent of its pulse cycle. Nevertheless both pulsars produce pulse bimodal profiles that have both a main pulse and interpulse. The lighthouse model attempts to explain such long duration emission by assuming that the pulsar's rotation axis is aimed almost directly toward the observer so that its radiation beam never disappears entirely from view as the neutron star rotates. However, lighthouse model theorists presume that the neutron star's rotation axis should instead be aimed almost *perpendicular* to our line of sight to produce an interpulse. In this way, oppositely directed beams would alternately sweep in our direction. So far no one has been able to resolve this spin axis orientation conundrum.

The pulsar PSR 0950+08 also poses a problem. Although this pulsar is observed to produce a distinct main pulse, close observation shows that it produces synchrotron radio emission *over its entire pulse cycle.* So, according to the lighthouse model, the neutron star's rotation axis should be aimed almost directly toward us, and so we should be seeing only one of the pulsar's two radiation beams. The other should remain hidden from our view. However, contrary to expectation, an interpulse is seen to follow its main radio pulse by about 42 percent of a pulse cycle (see figure 5), implying that we are seeing a second beam oriented 150° to the main beam.[5] This paradox has yet to be resolved.

Another perplexing feature of PSR 0950+08 is that its interpulse only shows up in a few percent of the pulse cycles. If this pulsar is a spinning neutron star, why would it be producing only one pulse the other 98 percent of the time? The lighthouse model offers little in the way of an explanation. As a result, together with the Crab and Vela pulsars, PSR 0950+08 stands as *one of the strongest pieces of observational evidence refuting the neutron star lighthouse model.* If these pulsars, are interstellar communication beacons, then the civilizations who created them should be commended for their ingenuity, for their signals have thrown astrophysicists and their models for a tailspin.

Uniform Emission of Cosmic Rays. PSR J0437-4715, the closest millisecond pulsar to our solar system, lies just 450 light years away in the constellation of Pictor.[6] Because of its close proximity astronomers have been able to obtain reasonably detailed radio telescope images of it. These show that it is closely orbited by a white dwarf star and that both are surrounded by a bow shaped shock front (figure 43) similar to that surrounding the EBM Pulsar (figure 19). Astronomers interpret this front as the boundary where the pulsar's cosmic ray wind confronts the surrounding gaseous interstellar medium as the pulsar plows forward. But the symmetrical shape of the bow front has led them to conclude that this pulsar, like the EBM Pulsar, *must emit its particle wind with equal intensity in all directions.* This, however, contradicts the theory that a pulsar is a neutron star that emits a pair of magnetically confined cosmic ray particle beams from either of its poles. If pulsars emit their cosmic ray particles evenly in all directions, how would their rotation produce brief radio pulses? The lighthouse model does not provide an answer.

Relativistic Rotation Problem. The spinning neutron star model was stretched close to its limit of credibility with the discoveries of the Millisecond Pulsar, PSR 1937+214, and the EBM Pulsar, PSR 1957+20, which spin respectively at 642 and 622 revolutions per second. The lighthouse model proposes these to be 20 kilometer diameter neutron stars spinning so fast that they have surface velocities of about *13 percent of the speed of light.* This is very close to the limiting velocity beyond which a neutron star would be made to fly apart. If the neutron star were indeed spinning at such a high speed, the forces generated by its rotation would be expected to continuously agitate the neutron star's magnetic field and cause large variations in the shape of the pulsar's time-averaged pulse profile. This problem is expected to be most severe in the case of the EBM Pulsar since its companion, which is separated from it by just one solar diameter, is obviously interacting quite strongly with the pulsar, being brightly illuminated by the pulsar's ionizing particle wind. However, as with most other pulsars, the pulse envelopes of these millisecond pulsars have a characteristic shape that does not change

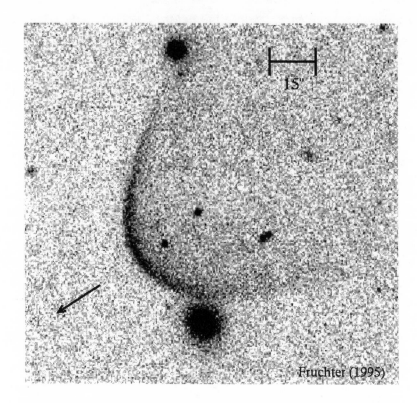

Figure 43. Optical image of the binary millisecond pulsar PSR J0437-4715 and its surrounding bow shock front taken through a red filter (15" = 0.03 light years). The white dwarf companion is visible as the faint star directly behind the shock. The pulsar lies at that same location, but is not optically visible. The arrow shows the direction in which the pulsar and its companion are moving in the plane of the sky (courtesy of Andrew Fruchter of STSI and the Cerro Tololo Inter-American Observatory).

over years of observation. In fact, the EBM Pulsar produces a main peak that has a duration of just 35 microseconds, two percent of its pulse period, which makes its profile one of the most precisely defined of all pulse profiles. The lighthouse model fails to account for the pulse profile constancy under such high speed conditions. This difficulty, however, is readily resolved if pulsars are theorized to be non-rotating communication beacons set up by alien civilizations.

Period-constancy Problem. Another unusual feature of milli-second pulsars is the extremely low rates at which their periods change. According to the classical lighthouse model, such rapidly spinning pulsars should have very high rates of energy loss through the production of gravity waves and electromagnetic radiation and hence should be slowing down rapidly. Calculations predict that the Millisecond Pulsar and EBM Pulsar, which presently have speeds of over 600 revolutions per second, should have slowed to about 100 revolutions per second in just one year.[7] Hence astronomers expected them to have the most rapid rate of pulse period lengthening of any pulsar, almost 1000 times that of the Crab pulsar. But just the opposite is found. The period of the EBM Pulsar lengthens at the extremely slow rate of just 1.7×10^{-20} seconds per second, or about half a picosecond per year. This is about 25 million times slower than the Crab pulsar's retardation rate. The Millisecond Pulsar has a comparably slow rate of change of just 1.05×10^{-19} seconds per second (3.3 picoseconds per year). In fact, the 20 most constant pulsars in the sky are all millisecond pulsars and hence behave contrary to theorist's expectations.

Astronomers also had supposed that pulsars with high spin rates should be relatively young, with millisecond pulsars being at most a few years old. If so, then they should be associated with a recent supernova explosion. But none of the 50 millisecond pulsars, discovered thus far, have been found to be anywhere near a young supernova remnant. Thus their discovery has proven to be quite troublesome for astrophysicists.

Spin Energy Dissipation Problem. Lighthouse model theorists believe that the explosive forces involved in compressing matter to neutron star densities would also compress and amplify any preexisting magnetic fields to very high values. So, they presume that a neutron star pulsar should have a very strong magnetic field. Moreover their calculations indicate that as the neutron star spins its rotating magnetic field will experience a dynamo braking force that will convert some of the star's rotational kinetic energy into electro-magnetic radiation. As a result, the neutron star would progressively slow down, and its pulse period would gradually lengthen. But, considering that pulsars have masses comparable to that of the Sun, they would have to be losing very large amounts of kinetic energy to accommodate their slow down rates. Lighthouse modelers, then, are forced to assume that their neutron stars must be radiating energy away at an enormous rate. To obtain an adequate braking force they assume that the neutron star has an excessively high magnetic field strength, ranging from a billion to one thousand trillion times the intensity of the Earth's magnetic field. This *assumed* magnetic field strength is about a billion times greater than field strengths normally observed in compact stars such as white dwarfs. But the main problem is that the power that must be radiated as a result of this hypothetical braking force is calculated to exceed by at least 1000 fold the amount of power being radiated in the pulsar's beamed emission.[8]

So where is the remaining 99.9% of the energy that the lighthouse predicts pulsars should be dissipating? If pulsars were to radiate this in the form of electromagnetic radiation, our radio telescopes should have seen it, and it should have been so intense as to completely mask the pulsar signals. But none is seen. If this missing energy instead went into accelerating cosmic rays, the acceleration process should produce large amounts of electromagnetic emission and again we should see something. But we don't.

The Crab pulsar presents an extreme example of this problem of the missing emission. If the cosmic rays illuminating the Crab remnant were being accelerated by the pulsar's spinning magnetic pole, the acceleration process should produce an electromagnetic emission equal to that coming from the entire remnant, but concentrated within a million kilometer diameter region centered on the pulsar. Our radio telescopes, which can resolve radio sources to an angle of at least one milliarc second, should then detect an unpulsed compact radio source having an intensity *one hundred billion times greater than that of the diffuse background emission from the Crab remnant, and over a trillion times greater than the pulsed radio signal coming from the Crab pulsar.* But, a radio source of such high intensity is not seen within the remnant.

The answer to this problem is simple. There are no "spinning neutron stars," rapidly dissipating their rotational energy. Pulsar radiation beams are stationary, and their pulse rates are precisely controlled by intelligent design, not by any phenomena of nature. As for the Crab Nebula, the cosmic rays that produce its diffuse emission originate from outside the remnant, not internally from a neutron star source.

Signal Ordering Too Complex to Explain

If a civilization wished to initiate communication with another civilization elsewhere in the Galaxy, it would want to send a signal that would not be mistakenly interpreted as coming from a natural object. Since most naturally occurring astronomical phenomena produce emissions that have a large degree of irregularity, a communicating civilization would want to make sure that their transmission was instead very highly ordered. In this respect, of all Galactic emission phenomena, pulsars seem to best fit the criterion of being of artificial origin. No other type of radiation source has been found to exhibit such precise time-ordering. Regular periodic variations in luminosity and color are known to occur in variable stars such as Cepheid variables, Mira variables, pulsating white dwarfs, and X-ray stars, but their pulsation periods are not nearly as accurate as those seen in pulsars. Some binary X-ray stars, for example, are known to pulse with periods as short as a few seconds, but their periods are accurate only to six or seven significant figures.* Pulsar periods, on the other hand, typically range from a million to one hundred billion times more precise. Moreover pulsating X-ray stars do not exhibit the rich variety of ordered behavior that is seen in the signals of radio pulsars. In instances where radio continuum emission is detected from such X-ray stars, the emission is usually highly erratic as is characteristic of stellar flaring. Such pulsating sources may truly be categorized as being of natural origin. Pulsars, on the other hand, are in an entirely different category. Their pulsation patterns are so highly ordered and so incredibly complex that attempts to describe them in terms of natural processes border on absurdity.

Let us review some of the ordering characteristics of pulsar signals. As was noted in chapter 1, the lighthouse model has difficulty accounting for even the most basic of pulsar signal characteristics such as explaining how the time-averaged pulse period is so precisely timed in view of the unusually large timing variability that characterizes the individual pulses. As we have seen above, the lighthouse model also has trouble explaining the period derivative characteristic, the gradual slowing of the pulsar's rate of pulsation. But, in addition, there is a great depth to the complexity of pulsar signals that poses equally grave difficulties for theories attempting to explain pulsars as being of natural origin. The great variety of signal ordering that is observed in pulsars is listed in Table 4 and treated in some detail in Appendix B. Some main points are summarized in the remainder of this section.

---

* Hercules X-1, for example, has a period of 1.237772 ± 0.000001 seconds, and Centaurus X-3 has a period of 4.843496 ± 0.000007 seconds.

TABLE 4
Kinds of Ordering Observed in Pulsar Signals

1. The 10 to 17 decimal place precise regularity of the pulsar's primary period, P_1, as determined from the timing of its time-averaged pulse profile.

2. The 6 decimal place precise regularity of the rate, $\dot{P}_1$, at which the pulsar's primary period increases over time.

3. The constancy of the shape and polarization of the pulsar's time-averaged pulse profile.

4. The ordering of successive pulses occurring within the same pulse cycle such that the pulses are always spaced from one another by a characteristic time interval, P_2.

5. The amplitude modulation of a sequence of consecutive pulses with a characteristic modulation period, P_3.

6. The occurrence of many pulse modulation frequencies in one pulse cycle with the modulation frequency being ordered with respect to pulse cycle phase. That is, a specific modulation frequency occurs only over a specific phase range.

7. The correlation of sequential pulse occurrences where a pulse occurring at one phase of the pulse cycle will be followed by a pulse occurring at a later phase of that pulse cycle.

8. The phenomenon of pulse drifting, whereby pulse sequences repeatedly scan across the time-averaged pulse profile with a characteristic repetition period, P_3.

9. Pulse "freezing" during nulling periods: the instance where the pulse signal becomes undetectable and pulse drifting ceases during an interval of time, after which drifting begins again where it left off.

10. Rapid amplitude modulation of a pulse's intensity, with the characteristic period, P_4, being on the order of tenths of a millisecond.

11. Mode switching, where the pulsar abruptly switches from one stable organized signal pattern (pulse profile) to one or more other stable organized patterns (pulse profiles).

12. The quantization of pulse drift rates, where the pulse drift rate doubles or triples in whole number multiples when the pulsar switches from one mode to the next.

13. Frequency dependent mode switching where the pulsar's mode switching is apparent only when the pulsar signal is observed within a certain radio frequency range.

14. Mode switching grammar, where mode switching is governed by rules that determine what mode the pulsar may switch to from any given mode that it happens to be pulsing in.

Pulse Amplitude Modulation. Although pulse timing and pulse amplitude change considerably from one pulse to the next, this variation is often found to occur in an ordered fashion. For example, in some pulsars the pulse intensity is observed to vary in a regularly timed manner, brightening for one or two pulses out of a long sequence of pulses. This pulse modulation typically occurs from 2 to 20 times slower than the repetition rate of the pulsar's *primary* pulse cycle.

To understand this layered ordering, imagine that you are looking through a rotating strobe wheel at a fluorescent light on a room ceiling. By rotating the strobe wheel at the proper speed and looking through its slits as they flash by your eye, you are able to match the frequency of the light as it flashes on and off 60 times per second. At this strobe speed, the flashing of the light will appear to you to have "frozen" in time. Depending on the phasing of the strobe relative to the light, the light will be seen either to be steadily illuminated at full brightness, steadily illuminated at semi-brightness, or steadily dark. Now, suppose that something has gone wrong with the central power generating station and that this causes the lights to momentarily brighten about five times every second. When we look through our strobe at the fluorescent light, we now see that its brightness is no longer constant, but that it flickers at a frequency of five Hertz. The 0.2 second period of this *amplitude modulation* would be found to be 12 times as long as the lamp's primary period which has a 1/60 second duration. This secondary amplitude modulation would be analogous to the pulse amplitude modulation we are talking about.

This amplitude modulation of the pulsar signal is also analogous to techniques commonly used in AM radio broadcasting. In this respect, the primary pulse repetition rate would be somewhat like the radio station's carrier frequency and the amplitude modulation of the pulsar's signal might be comparable to the amplitude modulation imposed on this carrier to broadcast music.

But pulsars can exhibit even more complex ordering, particularly those that have wide pulse profiles. For example, in some pulsars the period of this amplitude modulation can differ depending on the phase of the pulse cycle. For example, one might find that pulses appear 4 times per second near the beginning of the time-averaged pulse profile, 7 times per second near the end of the profile, and that they recur seemingly randomly in the middle part of the profile. Further complicating matters, two or more pulse modulation periods may be found to be present at any given phase of this pulse cycle. For example, one might find that pulses recur both 4 and 5 times per second near the beginning of the time-averaged pulse profile.

As yet another type of ordering, pulse modulation at one phase of the pulse cycle might be found to correlate with pulse modulation at another phase of the pulse cycle, but with a built in time lag so that a pulse occurring at one phase of the pulse cycle would be followed one pulse cycle later by a pulse occurring at another phase of the pulse cycle.

No natural stellar source is known to exhibit such highly organized signal characteristics, not even just one of these various types of pulse modulation. Astronomers seem to have taken for granted the idea that a natural object could conceivably produce such ordering since they have presumed that the unusual nature of this ordering might be attributed to the exceptionally high degree of matter ordering that is supposed to exist within a neutron star. So, as they catalog these various ordering characteristics, they think they are investigating the unusual conditions of ordering that they suspect might exist within a neutron star. But actually, they have no independent astronomical observations to confirm the assumptions they are making. When asked for proof of the existence of neutron stars, all they can point to is their pulsar observations, the very phenomenon they are attempting to explain in terms of their neutron star model. Neither have they conducted any experiments in the laboratory to determine if a naturally rotating particle beam could in fact generate such signal ordering. In the way of explanation, they confine themselves merely to the task of "modeling" a phenomenon that they a priori *presume* to be natural.

Pulse Drifting. Pulse drifting is a form of pulse amplitude modulation in which the pulse appears to "drift" across the time-averaged pulse profile. In other words its phase in the pulse cycle progressively changes with each successive pulse so that its position moves from the leading edge toward the trailing edge of the pulse profile, or in the reverse direction. As with pulse modulation, this pulse drifting phenomenon does not occur in a simple fashion. Often drifting is restricted to certain pulse cycle phases with drifting occurring at different rates depending on which part of the pulse cycle one happens to be analyzing.

Furthermore there are various types of drifting behavior. There is *linear drifting*, in which the pulse scans across the time-averaged pulse profile at a constant rate. There is also *nonlinear drifting*, in which the pulse drift rate changes, possibly beginning at a slow rate, gradually accelerating to a high drift rate, and then gradually decelerating to a slow drift rate. Again, just as the shape and timing of the time-averaged pulse profile remain exceedingly constant over time, so too these various specific characteristics of pulse modulation and pulse drifting do not vary from one year to the next. They are somehow programmed into each pulsar, providing each pulsar with a set of highly unique and unchanging signal characteristics.

If pulsar signals are of artificial origin, their authors have apparently done an excellent job of achieving a key objective in designing the ideal interstellar communication — namely, they have made the ordering of their transmissions so numerous as to confound astronomers' best attempts to ascribe the signals to a natural cause.

Pulse Nulling and Freezing. Some pulsars produce a temporary signal black out. One second they are transmitting at full intensity and the next second their signal has vanished. These so called *null periods* have been found to last for up to 8 hours or more. Careful studies of a few pulsars that exhibit this phenomenon show that during nulling the pulsar is still transmitting pulses, but at a very low intensity. Also observations have shown that during nulling the pulse drift rate becomes exceedingly slow. Consequently, when normal transmission resumes and the pulse drifting recommences at its normal rate, the pulses continue to scan the profile almost from the same pulse cycle phase they were in when they disappeared from view. Pulse nulling may be compared to the screen saver or energy saver feature on a home computer that lowers screen luminosity as a way of reducing the rate of energy consumption and extending the lifetime of the computer's cathode ray tube. The pulsar's freezing feature conveniently retards the pulse drifting activity during nulling with the result that little is missed during the interval that nulling is in progress. It is as if the pulsar "remembers" which phase of the pulse cycle its pulse had appeared in at the time nulling began. Theorists have met with considerable difficulty in their attempts to explain this nulling and pulse freezing phenomenon which must be included as one more ad hoc addition to their lighthouse model.

Mode Switching. Of the various pulsar signal-ordering phenomena, mode switching is probably one of the most interesting and most complex. Whereas most pulsars have one stable pulsation mode that persists seemingly indefinitely, in mode-switching pulsars, the normal pulsation mode might suddenly vanish and be replaced by a totally different and equally complex alternate mode. Whereas a particular mode of pulse ordering may last anywhere from 10 to 10,000 or so pulse periods, the transition from one mode to another may occur in as short a time as one pulse period. A mode switching event changes the entire character of the pulsar signal. Ordered patterns that normally remain remarkably invariant over many pulse periods suddenly terminate, and a new invariant pattern takes over. Mode switching alters the shape of the time-averaged pulse profile, restructures the pulse drifting and modulation behavior, alters the pulsar's polarization properties, and changes the way in which the pulse profile component intensities vary as a function of radio frequency.

To draw an analogy, a pulsar's time-averaged pulse profile might be imagined as being built up from its sequence of pulses in somewhat the same way that a fax machine's facsimile image is built up from its series of transmitted dots. Mode switching would be equivalent to the instance in which an entirely new fax image, or page, would begin to be transmitted. In spite of the radical changes involved in switching from one mode of signal ordering to another, the pulsar's exceedingly precise primary period and period derivative remain unchanged. This perplexing behavior has stymied astronomers attempts to come up with a natural explanation. In 1982, one group of pulsar investigators wrote:

> Despite the fact that the mode-switching phenomenon has such an important effect on pulse emission, no elaborate theory as yet exists as to how to interpret it.[9]

Frequency Dependent Mode Switching. In some pulsars the time-averaged pulse profile has the same form regardless of what frequency the pulsar is observed at. In other pulsars, the shape of the time-averaged pulse profile changes radically with observing frequency as does the number of components making up its profile. This is particularly apparent in the case of the Crab pulsar as was noted earlier. This frequency dependent effect becomes all the more mysterious in the case of mode switching pulsars. For example, in the case of the mode switching pulsar PSR 0329+54 not only does the profile have differing shapes at different observing frequencies, but also it has differing switching modes available to it at different frequencies.[10] When observed at frequencies ranging from 14.8 gigahertz* down to 5 gigahertz, the pulsar is found to

---

* One gigahertz equals 1000 megahertz.

switch between its normal mode and a single *abnormal* mode designated as mode A (see figure B.6 of Appendix B). At a frequency of 2.7 gigahertz, the pulsar is instead found to switch between its normal mode and either of two abnormal modes: mode A and a new mode designated as mode B. At a frequency of 1.4 gigahertz, switching is found to occur between the normal mode and *three* abnormal modes: A, B, and C. Proceeding to still lower frequencies the number of available modes declines again, only abnormal mode, B, being available at 0.83 gigahertz and only abnormal mode A being available at 0.41 gigahertz. Lighthouse models have not provided an adequate explanation for these unusual frequency dependent switching rules.

We are given to wonder whether there may be an intended logic behind the complex switching characteristics of this pulsar. That is, the pulsar seems to draw our attention to the 1.4 gigahertz frequency (21 centimeter wavelength) as being "more significant" than the rest since all three abnormal modes are available at that frequency and at no other. Interestingly, this is none other than the neutral hydrogen emission line frequency, the same frequency that SETI astronomers believe would most likely be used by alien civilizations for Galactic communication.

Mode Switching Grammar. In cases where pulsars have several modes available to them, switching from one mode to another sometimes conforms to certain fixed rules. One such pulsar, PSR 0031-07, can adopt any of three possible signal ordering modes: A, B, and C.[11] This pulsar emits bursts of pulses that are separated by null periods. During such a burst, rules come into play that govern how mode switching takes place. For example, if the pulsar is in mode A, it may switch to mode B within the same burst, or, if it is in mode B, it may switch to mode C within the same burst. However, the pulsar has never been found to switch from mode A to mode C in the same burst. Also rules appear to govern the rate at which pulses drift when each of these modes is dominant, modes A, B, and C having pulse drift rates that are whole number multiples of one another in the ratio of 1 to 2 to 3.

This quantized drifting behavior and mode switching grammar poses a serious problem to theorists who attempt to explain it as a natural phenomenon. Subatomic particles in the nucleus of an atom are known to be restricted to specific quantum energy states with specific rules governing their transitions from one energy state to another. Theorists have speculated that the neutrons composing a neutron star may reside in similar quantum states due to their highly compact condition. But to say that the same highly organized behavior should apply to the cosmic ray beam emitted from the surface of a hypothetical neutron star requires a very large leap of induction. Nuclear quantum ordering governs particles that are bound together by strong force fields, whereas the cosmic ray particles that are theorized to be generating the lighthouse model radiation beam are instead in high speed flight away from the star and hence would not necessarily reside in the same high density region. Moreover if we are to attribute pulse quantization and mode changing grammar to neutron star ordering, why is it not more prevalent among pulsars, but instead is unique to this particular pulsar?

Modeling Difficulties. The lighthouse model theorists have been quite at a loss to explain the numerous types of highly ordered phenomena that pulsars exhibit. Consider, for example, the question of pulsar memory. How does a mode-switching pulsar "remember" its former pulsation mode so that it can later switch back to it? Does the cosmic ray electron beam interact nonlinearly with the neutron star magnetic field so as to have various semi-stable *chaotic attractor* states each corresponding to a particular pulsation mode? Or, how does a pulse in a drifting sequence recall the phase of the preceding pulse so that it can become properly timed in the pulsation cycle and reproduce a drift velocity of a specific magnitude? And, how are such drift rates maintained over thousands of pulse sequences? Astronomers can only speculate since they have no laboratory data to back up this sort of behavior other than the pulsars themselves.

Some theorists have suggested models in which the pulse drifting phenomenon is due to cosmic ray discharges, or *sparks*, precessing about the neutron star's magnetic field pole. But theorists acknowledge that due to the turbulent polar field environment such precessing could be stable only for very short periods of time. Finally, how does a given pulsar modulate the phase and intensity of its pulses in such a way that the resulting time-averaged pulse profile has a specific shape and specific light polarization characteristics that remain invariant, or "remembered," throughout years of observation?

Pulsar astronomers Alexei Fillippenko and V. Radhakrishnan have been troubled by such considerations. In 1982 they wrote:

The standard polar cap [lighthouse] model of pulsar radio

emission provides acceptable explanations for a wide variety of observed pulsar characteristics. Nevertheless, we show that it has difficulty accounting for certain details pertaining to drifting subpulses, nulling, and mode changing. In particular, the persistence of drifting subpulse phase memory observed during pulsar nulling, as well as the phenomenon of nulling itself, seem to defy simple explanation.[12]

A number of qualitative modifications of the lighthouse model have been tentatively proposed in an attempt to account for these special types of ordering. However, so far no one has been able to bring these disparate revisions together into one coherent model. Pulsar astronomers Joseph Taylor, Richard Manchester and G. Huguenin also have expressed concerns about pulsar models:

> There exists an extensive literature of observational details which, although well substantiated by repeated measurements, remain unexplained and unassimilated into pulsar models.[13]

A theoretical model such as the lighthouse model not only provides astronomers with a framework for interpreting and comparing the various sets of observational data they come up with, but it also provides them with a common agreed upon context for sharing their ideas with one another, either in conversation or through publication. As a result, it serves a practical purpose. However, because of the sizable mental investment involved, astronomers hesitate to discard their model, even if it fails to account for observation. The lighthouse model, therefore, has evolved into a theoretical paradigm, a conceptual system having the unintended properties of self-stabilization and self-preservation. When new types of pulsar signal ordering are discovered which do not fit the lighthouse model, rather than seeking an alternative explanation, astronomers tend to elaborate their model or make special case modifications so that it might accommodate their new findings. Consequently, lighthouse models have grown unusually complex and varied, leaving pulsar astrophysics in a position similar to that of pre-Copernican astronomy which taught that the planets orbited the Earth in complex epicycle paths.

Each pulsar's signal is found to be highly ordered in a number of ways, and the manner of this ordering differs considerably from one pulsar to another making it impossible to conceive of a single neutron star model capable of encompassing the great variety of observed properties. On the other hand, such varied ordered complexity is exactly what one would expect if pulsars were in fact beacons used for interstellar communication or space navigation.

It is often said that one's first hunch is usually the right one. Few of the pulsar ordering properties that we know of today were known back in 1968 when the group of Cambridge University astronomers first published their pulsar discovery. At that time they knew just that the shape and pulse period of the time-averaged pulse profile remained highly invariant. If they had known then what we now know about pulsars, perhaps they would not have rejected the ETI communication scenario as readily as they did.

A "Low-tech" Particle Beam Communicator

Using presently available technology, it should be possible to construct a device capable of transmitting broadband interstellar signals much like those coming from pulsars. The technology required is the same as that used in particle accelerators employed by high-energy physicists for carrying out particle collision experiments. It is also the same technology used in particle beam weapons systems such as those developed in the Pentagon's Star Wars program. Except in this case the technology would be employed for peaceful purposes.

As mentioned earlier, a space-based particle beam communicator would consist of two main components: 1) a high-energy particle accelerator, and 2) a magnetic modulator unit for decelerating the particles and converting their kinetic energy into a beam of broadband synchrotron radiation (figure 1). The accelerator module would accelerate electrons very close to the speed of light (differing from light speed by only a few parts in 100 billion). At this speed they would have energies of about 100 billion electron volts, about 200,000 times greater than their rest-mass energy.

By comparison, the Stanford University linear electron accelerator used for carrying out high-energy particle collision experiments achieves electron energies of 50 billion electron volts. This device accelerates its particles by discharging electric power stored in enormous capacitor banks into metal collars positioned along the length of the accelerator tunnel. The steep electric field gradient induced within each collar gives the stream of particles a series of kicks that cause them to move forward at ever increasing speeds. The particles are then focused into a beam by a series of super-conducting electromagnet rings positioned at intervals along the tunnel, magnets that are so powerful that they require special spring-loaded restraints to prevent them from exploding when powered up.

Another type of particle accelerator has recently been developed which promises to vastly extend the present state of the art. This so called *beat-wave plasma particle accelerator* is able to generate accelerating energies per centimeter of tunnel length that are from 10,000 to 10 million times stronger than those used in the Stanford accelerator.[14] Two powerful laser beams of slightly differing frequencies are projected into a gas plasma tube to produce a "beat frequency wave" that moves through the plasma at a tremendous speed. Electrons "surfing" on this wave are then accelerated as the wave travels down the tube. A 10 meter long accelerator of this sort is theoretically capable of accelerating electrons to 100 billion electron volt energies.

Turning now to the particle beam modulator, which would be fixed at the output of the particle accelerator unit, this would consist of a long tunnel flanked on either side by a series of powerful super-conducting electromagnet coils. Their poles would alternate between north and south so that, when the coils were energized, the passing electrons would be deflected transversely, first one way and then the other, all the while maintaining their original straight-line course down the tunnel (figure 1). The electrons in the beam would emit broadband synchrotron radiation with each deflection. Due to their near speed-of-light velocity, they would project this radiation forward as *a very narrow beam*. Since the electrons would be traveling just about as fast as the beamed radiation, the emission contributed by each consecutive magnetic deflection along the length of the modulator tunnel would add up in phase to produce an extremely powerful laser-like beam.

By pulsing the electromagnetic modulator at regular intervals, the particle beam could be made to produce periodic bursts of synchrotron radiation. The bursts could be made to occur at extremely regular intervals simply by controlling the intensity of the beam modulator with a control unit timed by an atomic clock. Depending on how it was programmed, the control unit could generate the various pulse patterns and ordering phenomena observed in pulsars. It could produce a mode switching effect simply by flipping between alternate pulse contouring routines stored in its memory.

The energy of the beamed electrons and the strength of the modulator's magnetic field would together determine what part of the electromagnetic spectrum the synchrotron beam would most strongly radiate in. A communicator beacon using a bank of several particle accelerators, each producing an electron beam in a certain energy range and each having its own electron beam modulator, could be made to simultaneously project radio, optical, X-ray, and gamma ray pulses, producing pulse characteristics such as those seen in the Crab and Vela pulsars. Alternatively, a similar result might be accomplished by using a single particle beam with a multistage modulator that would apply deflecting fields of various strengths. With progressively stronger deflecting forces, the electron beam could be made to emit in progressively higher energy parts of the spectrum: optical, X-ray, or gamma ray.

Powered by a reasonably sized power source, such a particle beam communication device could transmit a broadband radio signal across a distance of several thousand light years and still yield a signal strength comparable to that detected from pulsars. It could even produce signals as intense as those coming from the Crab pulsar, one of the brightest pulsars in the heavens. At a distance of 6600 light years, a one megawatt synchrotron radiation beam projected from a 100 billion electron volt electron beam would yield a radio signal intensity comparable to that observed from the Crab pulsar which is situated at a similar distance (see appendix C). Although a radio power output of one megawatt is about ten times the power radiated by some of the larger commercial radio stations, still it is an easily achievable power level. By comparison, some of the larger nuclear power plants are able to produce over 1000 megawatts of power.

The power of the beamed synchrotron radiation is proportional to the cube of the particle energy. Hence a hundred thousand fold increase in particle energy translates into a hundred thousand fold narrower synchrotron beam and into a 10^{15} fold higher beamed radio signal intensity. The pulsed communicator radiation beam could easily be aimed so as to be visible to Earth observers. For example, if the beam was confined to a cone angle of just one second of arc, at a distance of 6600 light years, it would be visible from a region 0.03 light years across (1000 times the diameter of the Earth's orbit). Star tracking devices such as those used to aim the Hubble Space Telescope, could target the beam with an error of less than one percent of the beam's angular diameter.

The particle beam communicator model, described above and pictured in figure 1, is one that I had initially devised when I had begun suspecting that pulsars might be ETI communication beacons. For many years I thought that this was the only possible way to explain pulsars as an ETI phenomenon. At that time I thought that pulsar signals might be coming from communication beams projected from specially built space station installations. However, new data on binary pulsars that came out in the early 1990's forced me to abandon this design and confront the fact that pulsar signals must actually be coming from near the surfaces of very massive bodies. Such was implied from the cyclic variations in pulse period observed coming from pulsars that were in binary association with a companion star. By studying these variations, it is not only possible to determine the circularity of the companion's orbit, but also the companion's approximate mass and the mass of the pulsar. Invariably, the pulsar's mass turns out to be quite large, comparable with that of our Sun.

So, I realized that pulsar signals must necessarily be emitted in the rest frame of a very massive star, and cannot originate from the kind of space station outpost described above. Although such a communicator design could be used to produce beamed signals very much like those coming from pulsars, it could not account for the observation that pulsar signals come from bodies of celestial size.

Not having an adequate model, I began to consider the possibility that pulsars might be a natural phenomenon and that their conveyed message might reflect the presence of a high intelligence permeating the universe and attempting to make its presence known to us on a grand scale. However, shortly thereafter I thought of a different method of generating pulsar signals that made it possible to once again reconsider the hypothesis that pulsars might be artifacts of Galactic civilizations. Using this method an advanced civilization might actually engineer the cosmic ray flux coming from a star and cause it to emit a pulsed, collimated beam of synchrotron radiation. With sufficiently advanced technology, this should be possible. Let's examine one method.

Field-Engineered Stellar Cores as ETI Beacons

The first step in creating a pulsar communicator beacon would be to locate a suitable natural source of cosmic ray electrons. A white dwarf or X-ray star would be quite suitable. These are bare stellar cores that are left behind in the latter stages of a star's evolution. That is, as a star matures over billions of years of time, its dense metal-rich core grows increasingly massive and the energy flux from this core becomes increasingly intense.[15] Eventually, the outpouring of energy from its core is so great as to eject the star's gaseous envelope. This leaves behind an exceedingly hot, dense stellar core about the size of our Earth, but having a mass anywhere from a few tenths to somewhat more than one solar mass.

The core would be so hot that it would emit its energy as cosmic ray particles rather than as visible light. In some cases, where a stellar core is still surrounded by an atmosphere, its cosmic ray flux would excite visible, ultraviolet, and X-ray radiation. As such it would be classified as a white dwarf star. In other cases, where the core's atmosphere is more rarefied, the cosmic rays would be able to stream freely outward, exciting X-ray and perhaps gamma ray radiation, but little visible light. In such a case, the core would be classified as an X-ray star.* Unlike in the neutron star model that has the cosmic rays streaming out as confined beams, such stellar cores would radiate their cosmic rays fairly uniformly in all directions.

Neutron stars would most likely *not* be chosen as cosmic ray sources for the simple reason that they probably do not exist in nature, or if they do, they are probably extremely rare. Before the discovery of pulsars, neutron stars were only being considered by a few theoreticians. No neutron stars had been observed and probably for good reason. Being only 1 to 30 kilometers in diameter, a neutron star would be far too small to be resolved by our optical telescopes even if one were residing as close by as the nearest star. The only reason that astronomers began believing in their existence is that the neutron star lighthouse model could rotate very fast and hence could theoretically produce radiation pulses as rapidly as are seen coming from certain pulsars. However, as we have seen, the neutron star model has many pitfalls and, as noted in chapter 1, such a rapidly rotating cosmic ray source is not needed if pulsars are actually ETI beacons that produce their rapid flashes through magnetic field modulation. So if we abandon the lighthouse model and adopt the stationary beam ETI beacon interpretation, we eliminate the main reason for supposing that neutron stars exist.

Now suppose a civilization possessed a technology that allowed them to beam electric fields to a distant location in a manner not

---

* Although conventional astrophysics believes that bare stellar cores would be energetically dead and gradually cooling off, the physics of subquantum kinetics predicts instead, that they would be continuously generating energy in the form of cosmic rays. For more about this astrophysics consult the Author's books *Subquantum Kinetics* and *Beyond the Big Bang*.

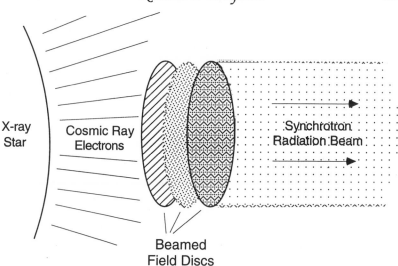

Figure 44. Field discs projected close to the surface of a white dwarf X-ray star for generating a stationary interstellar communication beam.

unlike the way radio signals are transmitted; not only to beam them, but also to cause them to revolve axially in such a way as to generate lines of magnetic force. Furthermore, suppose that, using this technology, this civilization had developed the means to generate such magnetic lines of force very close to the surface of the X-ray star. These might be configured as a series of discs measuring about 50 to 500 meters in diameter and several meters thick and oriented parallel to the star's surface (figure 44).

These fields need only have moderate strengths in the range of some tens of thousands of times the strength of the Earth's magnetic field. The incredibly strong magnetic fields that the lighthouse model uses in producing its synchrotron beams, fields 10^9 to 10^{15} times stronger than the Earth's field, are not mandatory in the ETI beacon model. Recall that lighthouse model theorists were forced to postulate enormous magnetic field intensities to secure a sufficiently strong spin braking force so that their model could account for the gradual lengthening of pulsar periods. There is no independent evidence that such strong fields exist, and as was discussed earlier, observational evidence instead suggests that such super strong magnetic fields *should not exist*.

As the star's outgoing cosmic ray electrons move through the telemetered magnetic field disc, they would emit synchrotron radiation and would beam this radiation in the direction of their outward flight. By deploying a succession of such discs of alternating magnetic polarity, the cosmic rays could be made to follow a straight-line flight path, and the radiation from these consecutive deflections could be made to add up to produce an intense beam of electromagnetic radiation capable of communicating over interstellar distances. Comparing this to the particle beam communicator design shown in figure 1, the X-ray star would serve the same function as the particle accelerator module and the telemetered fields would serve the same function as the particle beam collimator and modulator unit.*

By telemetering these field discs to the proper location on the star's surface, the synchrotron radiation beam could be aimed away from the star in any direction and targeted on a particular solar system hundreds or thousands of light years away. Moreover by properly modulating these fields, the beamed radiation could be made to produce precisely repeating pulses. The pulse period could be made to decrease at a precisely determined rate and to incorporate precise changes in timing and polarization so as to reproduce any of the pulse ordering properties observed in pulsar signals. Mode switching would involve simply changing the kind of information being telemetered to the surface of the star. The transmitter producing these fields could be situated at a safe distance from the X-ray star, perhaps positioned behind a distant planet or behind a force field shield where it might be sheltered from the outgoing cosmic ray wind.

A single X-ray star could be used as a power source to simultaneously beam messages to many locations around the Galaxy. Numerous field discs could be projected to different locations around the star, each creating a beam of synchrotron radiation targeted at a specific part of the Galaxy. Each pulsar might serve as a navigation nexus point that beams its signals to many different Galactic locations. Also each station might serve as a point for two-way communication, a kind of *Galactic internet node*, not only transmitting information but also receiving information from other locations using radio telescope apparatus. However,

---

* Interestingly, some elements of this model, such as the idea that "standing wave" field patterns modulate the pulsar's cosmic ray particle flux, have appeared in some versions of the lighthouse model; see the discussion of PSR 0826-34 given in Appendix B.

sending signals at superluminal speeds may require an entirely different type of communication apparatus.

Binary pulsars would present somewhat more of an engineering challenge. If the cosmic ray core star were orbiting a companion star, the synchrotron beam could be kept properly targeted on its destination by appropriately shifting the position of the telemetered fields so that they tracked the star throughout its orbit.

The power to maintain these projected fields could be derived from the X-ray star's cosmic ray wind. The energy of this outgoing particle flux could be tapped through conventional magnetohydro-dynamic techniques or through some more sophisticated means perhaps where the projected beam itself serves as the energy capturing net. Techniques to do this might be learned by pursuing research along the lines of the HAARP project, an abbreviation for High Frequency Active Aural Research Program.[16] This project, which is being carried out in Gakona, Alaska by the U.S. Department of Defense, attempts to use high frequency radio waves to create a large plasma layer 50 to 300 miles up in the Earth's ionosphere and to induce resonances in that layer that would couple with natural oscillations excited by the solar wind.

Could a civilization possessing advanced field projection techno-logies perhaps even engineer an entire supernova explosion? By establishing a field bridge between the two poles of a star and inducing a resonant electrodynamic oscillation between these two linked regions, the star might be induced to explode. Clearly, a civilization must reach a high degree of maturity if it is to wield such a technology. While it could be very beneficial if put to the proper use, it could also be used as a weapon of mass destruction if it fell into the wrong hands.

While all this may sound like science fiction, a technology for projecting force fields to remote locations has been developed and tested by the military. More is said about this in the next chapter.

Chapter 8

Force Field Beaming Technology

Aerial Plasmoids

As described in the previous chapter, it should be possible to produce decelerating forces on an X-ray star's outward flux of cosmic ray electrons by artificially creating electrodynamic force fields near the star's surface thereby producing a narrow beam of synchrotron radiation. Moreover by properly controlling these fields it should be possible to modulate the intensity of this beamed radiation continuum to produce pulses for interstellar communication or spacecraft navigation. If it were possible to telemeter force-inducing fields over interplanetary distances, say over several astronomical units (one A.U. being the distance from the Earth to the Sun), then such a feat could be possible.

Actually, the U.S. military is rumored to be testing a technology for application to warfare that could be doing precisely this — transmitting force-exerting fields to distant locations.[1] However, these methods would have to be deployed on a far larger scale if they were to be used for interstellar communication, or for creating a superwave shield. Although details of the technology are immersed in secrecy, its existence is evident from numerous sightings of strange luminous spheres being seen in the night or evening sky. The devices that produce these effects are apparently able to ionize the atmosphere to such an extent as to form a luminous ball of plasma. These so called *plasmoids* resemble in some respects the appearance of ball lightning, only they are far larger.

They are most probably generated by microwave beams. In his article in *Nexus* magazine, Harry Mason quotes part of a December 1996 Voice of Russia interview with the Russian science authority Boris Belitsky. Belitsky stated that in the 1993 Vancouver Summit the U.S. and Russia had proposed to cooperate in the testing of microwave weapons, and when the correspondent asked him how a microwave generator might be used as a weapon, Belitsky responded:

It would be used to fire a plasmoid — that is, a blob of plasma — into the path of an incoming missile, its warhead, or an aircraft. The plasmoid would effectively ionize that region of space and, in this way, disturb the aerodynamics of the flight of the missile, warhead or aircraft and terminate its flight. This makes such a generator and its plasmoid a practically invulnerable weapon, providing protection against attack via space or the atmosphere.[2]

A sighting of one version of this novel technology occurred in the Superstition Mountains near the town of Apache Junction which lies about 25 miles east of Phoenix, Arizona.[3] Elizabeth, her husband Dale, and their daughter Alicia had gone camping one weekday in the spring of 1993. Driving seven miles off the main road, they reached the campground parking lot at dusk. Leaving their car behind, they hiked up a canyon into the mountains, and after journeying about a third of a mile they set up camp. It was nearing 11 PM as they bedded down and began watching the stars in the beautiful desert night. They were the only ones out there. A wind was blowing, which thankfully was keeping the mosquitoes at bay. Alicia commented about how unusual this was, because she had gone camping in these same mountains a week before and had been eaten up by the mosquitoes.

As they were lying there, they were startled by a loud low rumbling, which sounded like distant thunder. But the sky was cloudless. A few minutes later, looking down the canyon, they were amazed to see a huge aura of white light begin to fill the sky over the distant parking lot. It gradually brightened, looking like the kind of light that is seen filling the sky over a lit ballpark stadium. Some minutes later a fiery ball of white light rose from behind the mountain ridge on the far side of the parking lot and hung about 20 feet above the ridge casting an eerie white light over the surrounding landscape. The sphere appeared to be about 2 degrees of arc in size (several full moon diameters), which means that at that distance it would have measured about 60 feet in diameter. Being somewhat brighter than the full moon, it lit up the sage brush and could be seen reflecting off their faces and clothing. It disappeared from view a couple of times, but came back up. After five or ten minutes of this, the sphere then retreated behind the mountain, the aura faded away, and all became quiet again.

About 15 minutes later the rumbling began again and the aura of light reappeared. Within minutes a ball of light emerged again from behind the mountain. But this time after clearing the ridge it moved to the left along the ridge and then veered out into the middle of the canyon hovering about three to four hundred feet above the ground surface. They realized that what they were witnessing could not have been produced by an ordinary searchlight. After some time, the sphere retraced its path, disappeared behind the ridge, and the aura once again faded away.

After another lapse of time, they again heard the rumbling sound. Again the sky lit up with a diffuse light. This time four luminous balls rose into the sky and lined up horizontally across the ridge. Then this horizontal formation moved to the middle of the canyon where the spheres later moved to a vertical orientation. Then while still in full view, they suddenly disappeared. Then, in the blink of an eye, they reappeared in different positions. After some additional maneuvering, they again disappeared and the aura subsided. This sequence of events recurred several more times, the aura appearing, the multiple spheres emerging, moving in the sky, sometimes blinking out, the spheres retracting behind the ridge, and the aura subsiding. The entire display had lasted slightly over two hours. When the aura had faded for the last time, the campers noticed that the wind also had ceased to blow and the mosquitoes had begun to invade their camp. To this day they have no explanation for the awesome sights they witnessed that night in the desert mountains.

Similar aerial electromagnetic technology displays have been seen in Australia. In a four year period between May of 1993 and May of 1997 there were over 1000 reports of aerial "fireballs" and associated luminous energy emissions that followed long trajectories over various parts of Australia. In his Nexus article, Harry Mason explains:

> These fireballs have been observed in all our Australian states. . . and in many cases have exhibited variations on and combinations of the following actions: very-low-altitude; nap-of-the Earth trajectories; small-to-nonexistent tails; no fragment drop-off; apparent velocity often very slow and commonly less than that of sound; no associated sonic booms; considerable and sudden changes in course, as well as speeding up, stopping dead, reversing course and flying vertically upwards into space; creation of intense vibration of ground and housing during flypast; explosion in massive blue-white arcing light displays with major explosive sound events or silent, intense light-flashes; regular creation of power generation overvoltage outages and other electrical effects.[4]

He describes eyewitness reports of one event that took place on May 28th, 1993. About an hour before midnight, a large, luminous plasmoid, or "fireball," was seen to fly from south to north in a low trajectory that was nearly parallel to the Earth's surface. It traveled about 1 to 2 kilometers at a subsonic speed similar to that of a 747 jet and emitted a pulsed roaring sound as it went. Some described it as an orange sphere with a small bluish-white conical tail, others said it was cylinder shaped and yellow-blue-white in color. Its low speed and near horizontal trajectory ruled out natural phenomena such as meteors as a possible cause. Upon impacting the ground, the fireball produced a near blinding high energy burst of blue-white light that rippled for three to five seconds. Witnesses said that the illumination was as bright as day, allowing them to see for some 100 kilometers in all directions. The blast, heard up to 250 kilometers away, is estimated to have had an energy of more than two kilotons of TNT. A one-kilometer-diameter luminous hemisphere, deep-red-orange in color with a silvery outer lining, then arose and hovered above the explosion site, bobbing around for almost two hours before suddenly disappearing. The impact site was located by triangulation from seismograph records and from eye witness accounts. However, careful examination of the site revealed no sign of any crater.

Mason reports another incident that occurred one night in mid-October of 1994 in the Western Australian town of Tom Price. Residents reported seeing a red-orange fireball with a central "flame-engulfing black hole," cruising at about 100 miles per hour at an altitude of a few hundred meters. It was seen to be followed at evenly spaced intervals by two other fireballs tracking along the same trajectory. All appeared to originate from a military installation on the Exmouth Peninsula that was once a US VLF radio communications base, but whose operation had later been turned over to the Australian government.

Microwave Phase Conjugation

The microwave generators that create these plasmoids may operate using the principles of *optical phase conjugation*.[5,6] The term "phase conjugation" refers to a special kind of "mirror" that is able to reverse the trajectories of the incident light waves and cause them to precisely retrace the path they followed to the phase conjugating mirror. The outcome is as if the photons had been made to travel *backward* in time. If you shine a flashlight beam at an angle toward a regular silvered mirror, the beam will reflect off at an equal angle in the opposite direction. But if you angle a flashlight beam at a phase conjugate mirror, the returned beam will instead shine directly back at your flashlight!

Optical phase conjugation is most commonly known for its use in military laser weapons systems for destroying enemy missiles. In this application, a laser beam is directed at a distant moving missile target and light rays scattered back from the target are allowed to enter the phase conjugator, a chamber containing a medium having nonlinear optical properties. In this nonlinear medium, the scattered rays interact with two opposed laser beams of a similar wavelength to form a hologram-like electrostatic light refracting pattern called a "grating." Once this grating pattern is formed, the system has essentially locked onto its target. A powerful laser weapon is then discharged into this holographic grating pattern, whereupon the coherent laser light reflects in such a way as to produce an intense outgoing laser beam that retraces the paths that had been followed by the incoming rays that had originally been scattered from the missile. Consequently, the outgoing laser pulse converges precisely back onto its missile target.

The microwave counterpart of a laser is called a maser. Just as a laser produces a coherent beam of light radiation, so too a maser produces a coherent beam of microwave radiation. Consequently, it should be possible to phase conjugate microwaves, by following techniques similar to those described in experiments with optical phase conjugation. However, it appears that most of this research is still highly classified. While many papers have been published on optical phase conjugation, virtually no literature is available on the application of phase conjugation at microwave frequencies. Nevertheless, by applying basic phase conjugation concepts, it may be possible to reverse-engineer some aspects of this microwave technology to get a rough idea of how it might work.

For example, suppose that a bank of high-voltage capacitors are suddenly discharged to momentarily create a powerful air ionizing arc, or irregularly shaped plasmoid. Also, suppose that a beam of coherent microwave radiation from a maser is targeted on this plasmoid. This beam would be sent out by a phase conjugating device something like that pictured in figure 45. This device splits the original maser beam into two beams, a *probe beam* and a *pump beam*. The probe beam is directed toward the plasma target, and some of its scattered microwaves shine back toward the phase conjugator device and enter its *mixer* chamber. The mixer chamber is filled with a medium that has very nonlinear electromagnetic

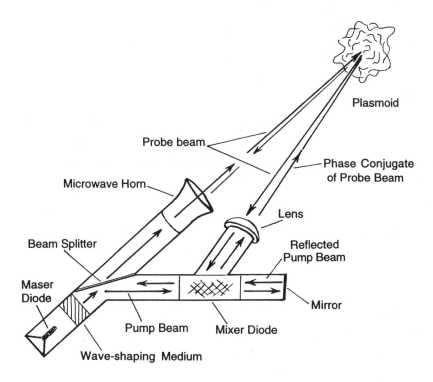

Figure 45. Proposed schematic of a phase conjugate microwave resonator and associated aerial plasmoid.

properties. Meanwhile, the pump beam that is split off from the maser generator is directed to the adjoining mixer chamber where it passes through the nonlinear mixer medium, reflects from a wall at the far end, makes a second pass back through the mixer medium, and then reenters the maser generator compartment.

The microwaves that scatter from the plasmoid and enter the mixer medium strongly interact with the two pump maser beams to form an electrostatic grating pattern. This holographic pattern stores information about the directions and phases of all the scattered maser beam microwaves that have entered the mixer. The counterpropagating pump beams then reflect from this grating pattern to produce an outgoing microwave beam that *precisely traces the paths followed by the incoming scattered waves*. In this way, the outgoing microwaves converge back on the plasmoid, and from there travel back to the maser device from which they originated, the randomizing effects of any wave scattering having been automatically compensated for.

Physicists would call this return beam the phase conjugated probe beam, or simply, the *phase conjugate beam*. The term "phase conjugate" signifies that the trajectories of the microwaves are identical to those that would be followed if the incoming probe beam microwaves had been made to travel backward in time. The grating that performs this time-reversed reflection is called a *phase conjugate mirror* and the mixing arrangement that allows all this to happen is termed a *four wave mixer*. Although the maser transmitter and four wave mixer cavity are shown in figure 45 as being separated from each other, with proper engineering it should be possible to combine them into a common maser transmitter/receiver apparatus.

After the phase conjugate beam returns to its maser source, it reflects back from the maser's end mirror, travels out once again as a coherent beam, scatters off from the plasmoid, and again returns to the mixer chamber. This closed loop path from the maser beam generator, to the plasmoid, to the mixer, to the plasmoid, and back to the maser beam generator, causes the maser system to function as a *phase conjugate resonator* and to *preferentially select and amplify only those microwaves that target the phase conjugating mixer chamber*. As a result, most of the microwave power emitted from the maser will end up being confined to a beam that extends between the maser beam generator, the plasmoid target, and the mixer chamber. The energy bottled up in this beam will then progressively build up to a very high value.

Thus unlike a conventional maser, which emits a nonreturning energy pulse that eventually scatters into space, a phase-conjugating maser instead preserves the majority of its energy in an enduring beam that extends between the maser and its target. A portion of the maser beam energy, though, will go into heating the plasmoid. Also to a lesser extent, some energy will be lost due to inefficiencies in the maser mixer cavity. The phase conjugator will tend to amplify those microwave trajectories that are most efficiently scattered back from the plasmoid. So, there will be a tendency for the beam's energy loss to the plasmoid to be minimized. However, if the plasmoid were to intersect a solid target, the enormous energy stored up in the beam would suddenly be absorbed by the target, resulting in the target's destruction.

Tom Bearden, who has written several books and papers about this microwave technology, believes that many of the unusual luminous aerial phenomena that have been observed are produced by military tests of phase-conjugating masers.[7,8] He points out that the incoming probe beam and its returned phase conjugate beam would precisely superimpose with one another so as to mutually cancel their transverse force vectors. The two beams in combination would consist of *energy potential waves* (e.g., electrostatic charge density waves). Since energy potentials have magnitude, but no direction, physicists term such waves — *scalar waves*, to distinguish them from Hertzian electromagnetic waves which have a transverse vector polarity. Consequently, the phase-conjugating maser would produce a stationary *scalar wave* beam between itself and the plasmoid which would remain largely invisible to normal means of detection.

Bearden further maintains that if two such scalar wave beams are made to intersect, the interlocked probe and phase conjugate beams would decouple from one another in this intersection zone allowing normal electromagnetic waves. Plasmas have nonlinear electromagnetic properties. Hence if two such scalar beams were made to intersect a plasmoid, the nonlinear plasma environment might cause them to interact with each other sufficiently to "unmask" part of their energy. Consequently, by choosing slightly different frequencies for the two maser beams and modulating their amplitudes in the proper fashion, it should be possible to conduct interferometry and to thereby control the shape, size, intensity, and location of the plasmoid, similar to what Bearden has suggested.

Tesla Waves

A phase conjugate maser may be able to transmit energy to a distant target or extract energy from that target through energy exchange with the target. However, to exert mechanical forces on a distant target, or for that matter to exert forces on distant cosmic rays, it is necessary to use a microwave source that radiates microwave frequency shock pulses having a sawtooth shaped waveform, rather than a sinusoidal waveform typical of conventional electromagnetic waves. The force exerting ability of electrodynamic shocks was first discovered by Nikola Tesla in the late nineteenth century. Tesla designed multimillion-volt radio frequency generators that created these waves by charging up a high-voltage capacitor bank and repeatedly discharging it through a spark gap into a primary coil winding. By inductively coupling the primary to a secondary coil and further to a third coil which he termed the "extra coil" which was connected to a vertical antenna mast, he was able to step up the voltage of these shocks to millions of volts. His generators are today called Tesla coils.

These repeated discharges generated sawtooth pulses that began with an abrupt rise in voltage lasting a few nanoseconds, followed by a gradual voltage relaxation that transpired over a period of 1 to 10 microseconds. The pulses repeated with a frequency of about 0.1 to 1 megahertz and were conducted upward to a crowning spherical terminal from where they radiated into space. These "Tesla waves" differed from conventional Hertzian electromagnetic waves in that their field potentials consisted of purely longitudinal energy potential gradients with no transverse component. Tesla viewed them as alternate compressions and rarefactions that move longitudinally through a gas-like ether medium in much the same way that sound waves move through air. As discussed in chapter 2, conventional Hertzian waves and Tesla waves both find adequate description in the methodology of subquantum kinetics.[9]

Tesla found that when he stood near these shock discharges he could feel them as a great force or sharp pressure striking the whole front of this body.[10] These effects were most apparent as a stinging of the face or hands, which persisted even when he situated himself behind glass and metal shields as far as 50 feet from the shock source. He was able to collimate these wave discharges by energizing a terminal placed at one end of an open ended tube. The tube emitted a ray beam *that was able to push objects*, charge objects, or burn holes through objects depending on their composition. For some of his experiments, Tesla fabricated these ray tubes as heavy-walled glass vacuum tubes. On some occasions, they experienced such a high outward pressure when energized that they would explode, in spite of their high vacuum.[11] Tesla ascribed these forces to the action of ether currents propelled forward by the ether shocks he was producing. Although, it is possible that the shocks themselves were the cause, a forward longitudinal force being more efficiently applied by the initial shock front and less efficiently counteracted by the more gradual relaxation gradient that followed.

Tesla found that his shock beams did not diverge like normal electromagnetic emissions, but remained collimated and coherent over great distances much like modern maser beams. If so, then perhaps optical phase conjugation might be achieved just as easily with a Tesla shock wave generator as with conventional lasers or masers which produce beams of sinusoidal Hertzian waves. Perhaps phase conjugation could explain how his Colorado Springs tower was able to transmit such an enormous amount of power to a receiver station located 26 miles away. Despite its great distance, the receiver tapped about 10 kilowatts of high-frequency power, enough to illuminate 200 50-watt bulbs to bright incandescence.[12] If his transmitted power had dropped off according to the inverse square of distance, as it does for normal radio broadcast, his receiver should have picked up microwatts, not kilowatts. The matter is more readily explained if Tesla's receiver had established a beam-like link with the transmitting tower through the phenomenon of phase-conjugate resonance.

The twentieth century German scientist Rudolph Zinsser also discovered that sawtooth waves could be made to push distant objects.[13] He produced a radio tube circuit that transmitted 45 megahertz radio waves having a sharp rise and gradual fall. His experiments demonstrated that these waves could exert impulses of up to 10^4 to 10^5 dyne seconds, which is equivalent to the application of about 1 to 3 ounces of force for a period of one second. This *kineto-baric force*, as he called it, could be generated with an amazingly low input power, amounting to just 6 newton seconds per watt second. Or, in other words, this meant that it should be possible to produce a 135 pound force with an input power of just 100 watts! Zinsser remarks that this output-force–to–input-power ratio "surpasses that of conventional propulsion methods *by several powers of ten*." Moreover, like Tesla, he found that the force was cumulative, each sawtooth wave impulse adding to its predecessor. Mysteriously, he also found that the force continues to affect the target mass even after the transmitter is shut off, the effect having a characteristic decay time constant. Zinsser received a U.S. patent on this sawtooth generator invention in 1978 (No. 4.085,384).

Solid state crystal devices called IMPATT diodes have been developed which produce sawtooth-like shock emissions, much like those that Tesla and Zinsser were producing, and pulse at microwave frequencies, rather than at radio frequencies. They operate on the electron avalanche principle wherein the diode, which initially presents a very high resistance, becomes a good conductor once a critical threshold voltage is surpassed. Past this threshold, an electron avalanche current is suddenly released, creating shock front that moves down the length of the diode. Although IMPATT diodes on the open market operate at only several hundreds of volts, diodes rated for much higher voltages and power outputs quite likely are produced for restricted military use. By using such a solid state device in place of a maser, it should be possible to produce a microwave phase conjugator that generates Tesla shock wave beams, rather than Hertzian beams. In which case, it would be possible to produce phase conjugate beams capable of transmitting force fields to distant locations.

Deployed on a much larger scale with properly controlled interferometry, such a beam technology could be used to establish electrostatic field gradients near the surface of an X-ray star for deflecting outgoing cosmic ray electrons and thereby producing a synchrotron communication beam. Moreover, pertaining to the ETI message, a similar technology could be used to set up a cosmic ray deflecting force field shield capable of protecting a planet or even an entire solar system from an advancing superwave.

The Crop Circle Phenomenon

Other evidence of the existence of a field projection technology similar to that used in producing plasma fireballs may be found in the phenomenon of crop circles. Crop circles are large highly organized patterns, usually appearing in fields of grain, such as grass, wheat, barley, or corn, where the crops have become mysteriously flattened to the ground in a very short time (see figure 46). Often the matted areas have the form of circles or rings, but they can also appear as rectangles, linear swaths, or arc-like shapes. Based on the various characteristics that have been reported, crop circle researchers have concluded that the circles are formed by some kind of advanced microwave beam technology.

Most crop circles appear overnight although some have been reported to form in full daylight. One formation appeared in a field in between successive aerial surveillance flights spaced just half an hour apart. Crop circle researcher Colin Andrews reports that of a group of seventy people who claimed to have witnessed crop circles in the process of being formed, all agreed that the laying of the crop occurred in no more than 15 seconds! They described the event as being preceded by a sudden silencing of the song birds, the stillness in the air being broken by a "trilling sound" accompanied by the sound of wheat heads banging together, despite an absence of wind. In one case the sound was captured on magnetic tape, and subsequent analysis found it to be beating at a frequency of 5.2 kilohertz.

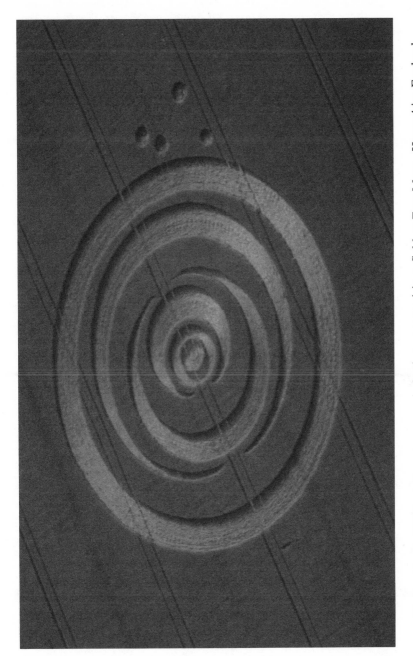

Figure 46. A 100 foot diameter crop circle that appeared in a field at East Meon, Hampshire England in July of 1995 (photo by Ron Russell).

Crop circles have been observed since the 1970's, with the documented sightings now numbering over ten thousand. Although most of the occurrences have taken place in the British Isles, formations have also been reported in the U.S., Canada, Australia, New Zealand, Tasmania, France, Switzerland, Russia, and Brazil. In earlier years the designs were relatively simple, consisting mainly of circular matted regions. Later, more elaborate designs began to appear, such as circles surrounded by a series of concentric rings. Often several circles might be found clustered together to form well-defined geometrical patterns, sometimes interconnected by perfectly straight "avenues."

Beginning in 1990, the crop circle phenomenon dramatically intensified. Not only was there an exponential increase in their numbers, but also there was a dramatic increase in the size of the patterns. Every year heralded the appearance of new types of designs. Whereas earlier designs consisted mostly of simple circle and ring patterns ranging up to about 20 meters in diameter, now, patterns began appearing which stretched out over several hundred meters. Moreover these new designs were far more complex.

Although disposed in two dimensions, some of the new patterns represented higher dimensional fractal forms like the "Mandelbrot set" crop glyph. The Mandelbrot set is generated by performing a specific mathematical operation on a complex number and repeating the operation by taking the product of the previous calculation and using it as input for the next calculation. Two of these complex patterns appeared in wheat fields in 1991, one in Ecleton, England and the other at Barbury Castle, Wiltshire, England. Equally complex crop circle fractals depicting the Julia set appeared in July 1996. A single Julia set spiral composed of 151 circles stretching out over a diameter of 400 feet appeared in a wheat field near the ancient monument of Stonehenge. That same month a triple Julia set spiral appeared in a wheat field at Windmill Hill, England. It was composed of 194 circles that stretched out over a distance of 700 feet.

Within a crop circle's compacted region, the plant stems are found compressed to the ground so firmly as to leave their indentations in the soil, yet their stems are not broken or damaged. They sometimes splay radially outward from the circles' centers, but more often are angled so as to form Archimedian spirals, sometimes proceeding clockwise, other times counterclockwise, and on occasion a combination of both. The combined contrarotating spirals

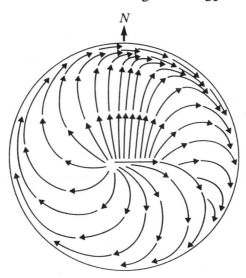

Figure 47. Schematic of a crop circle that appeared at Cheesefoot Head, England in 1987 (Delgado and Andrews, *Circular Evidence*, p. 128).

are particularly perplexing because the direction of the rotary lay abruptly flips at a well-defined boundary. On one side of this border, a stem would lie in one direction while its immediate neighbor on the other side of the border would lie in the opposite direction.

The crop circle that appeared at Cheesefoot Head in 1987 exhibited a clockwise spiral pattern that was deformed in the circle's northern sector to form a radial swath directed northward (see figure 47). Near the center of the circle, this north-aligned pattern made a surprisingly sharp 90° flip transition to the spiral pattern. Yet another spiral crop formation had a central patch measuring two meters square in which the stems all faced in the same direction with the spiral pattern emerging outward from the square's periphery.

Braided or plaited lay patterns have also been found in which bundles of stems have been left overlaying one another in alternating directions, giving the appearance of a basket weave when viewed from afar. Crop circle researchers have puzzled over how these complex weaves could be formed. In their book *Circular Evidence*, researchers Pat Delgado and Colin Andrews state:

> Some of the bundles have had two or more bundles laid at differing angles over and under them so that they are actually intertwined. The force field that produced this would have to be operating like a knitting machine. On two occasions, in two different circles, some bundles of these braids have been laid in

opposition to each other. There seems to be no limit to the complication of lay that this extraordinary unknown force can produce.[14]

Even more detailed crop knitting has been noted. For example, crop circle researcher Ilyes observes that the crop within a Circle is laid in bundles composed of anywhere from a few plant stalks to as many as forty or fifty.[15] The stalks in a bundle are aligned parallel to one another and are bound together by their leaves which wrap around in criss-crossing fashion. Ilyes notes that, outside the crop circle perimeter, the seed heads of the standing crop are randomly oriented. On the other hand, within each bundle, the seed heads are parallel to one another, as if commonly aligned by an applied force.

More than just mechanical force is involved in creating the crop formations. There is overwhelming and consistent evidence that the crop has been heated during the crop circle forming process, for expulsion cavities called "blown nodes" are seen at the sides of individual stalks. Biophysicist Dr. W. C. Levengood produced similar results in the laboratory by inducing a very rapid rate of heating.[16] Ilyes postulates that crop circles are formed by a microwave maser beam projected down from above and that associated cellular heating effects cause the fluid within the plant cells to expand and erupt through a node or joint in the stalk's surface. She also suggests that the crop stalks suddenly wilt and become supple as their plant cells dehydrate and expand during this brief heating phase. In this way they are susceptible to being reoriented by the applied force, without being broken.

Other tests carried out by Levengood have shown that the molecular and cellular structure of the plants has become substantially changed with distinct signs that they have been exposed to transient high temperatures.[17] Seeds taken from inside a crop circle formation have been found to be altered both with respect to their growth rate and their mode of germination. When the seeds are planted, their growth rates in some cases are seen to have become increased by as much as 45%. Moreover, extended observation of the crop circles shows that, once the plants have been laid flat by this force, their head ends never attempt to grow vertically again.

Researchers have found that crop circles are pervaded by a residual energy field that remains for some weeks after the circle's formation, an effect reminiscent of Zinsser's observations of a "residual force." Investigators Ron Russell and Dr. Simeon Hein have used a portable TREK-520 electrometer to make electric field measurements of several crop circles in the Wiltshire, England region.[18] Their findings indicated the presence of a "membrane" at the outer edge of crop circles, across which the measured field energy shifts first lower, then perceptibly higher. These spike-like energy variations were also found in the interiors of crop circle, at the edges of internal details, and especially at the centers of the circles. They found that they had to wait several days before entering a newly formed crop circle because otherwise the field energy would cause their electronic equipment to malfunction and their power supply batteries to rapidly drain. It is commonly reported that the batteries of cell phones, GPS devices, magnetometers, video cameras and tape recorders drain rapidly within crop circle formations. This calls to mind reports of car engines stalling and radios going dead during UFO close encounters.

The unusual growth phenomena, residual fields, and complex way in which the compaction patterns are formed have led researchers to conclude that crop circles cannot have been produced by common hoaxers using simple hand tools. Delgado and Andrews summarize the crop circle phenomenon as follows:

> Any specification for a force that can produce all these complications will have to include the following features: flattening crop stems of various thicknesses hard to the ground without damage, spiral whorl rotation, contra-rotation, multilayering containing multi-direction lays, blast-effect radial swathes, and all the different central area formations. Not only must the force be able to lay the crop in either direction of rotation, it must be able to do both rotations without gradation on the floor of the same circle.

> It must be a strong force of short duration that induces horizontal growing into the plant, replacing its natural tendency to the vertical... It must also be able to make the root end of thick-stemmed plants pliable enough to bend to a sharp, almost 90° angle, without fracturing and disturbing the plants' growth rate.

> It must be able to construct a flattened ring around the outside of a circle, closely following the contour of the circle wall. Besides creating circular shapes, it must also be able to flatten a dead straight pathway several meters long. It should have the ability to miss narrow, arc-shaped areas of crop and so leave these stems standing, like a low, slim, curved screen. It must be so violent that some plants are pulled up randomly or ejected from the soil and thrown into the peripheral standing crop. It must be quiet.

> It is very sobering to stand in one of these circles and ponder what force could have arrived and departed, leaving behind this beautiful record of its visit with no clue as to how it was achieved.[19]

One farmer who witnessed the creation of a ringed circle in his small corn patch in Romania described the force as so strong that it tore away his hat and flung him to the ground. It was accompanied by a "terrible whistling sound."[20] This same force could explain why a jack rabbit carcass was found inside one crop circle dehydrated and *compressed to a pancake*. Also crop circle researcher Donna Higbee describes several cases in Canada and England in which crop circles have been found to contain compressed porcupines. Porcupines, which normally stand at least 12 inches tall, have been compressed down to *two to three inches* by some tremendous force. She notes that porcupines stay put when they detect danger, relying on their sharp quills for defense. Hence there is less likelihood that they would flee at the time the circle was being formed. Higbee also reports instances in which porcupines were forcefully dragged into a crop circle. She states:

> Also, there have been at least two cases where a skid mark in the soil, embedded with broken quills, showed the unfortunate porcupine had been dragged by force from the edge of the formation into the center. Its quills were oriented in the same direction as the swirled wheat.[21]

A technology capable of projecting a force field to a remote farm field to bend stalks of wheat or blades of grass could also be made to project a force field that could bend the trajectories of cosmic ray particles in space. Moreover a force field technology able to create intricate patterns in fields of vegetation could also be made to modulate forces near the surface of a cosmic ray emitting star to produce synchrotron pulses similar to those observed coming from pulsars. Are the hundreds of crop circles being produced each year the result of force field projection experiments being carried out by our own scientists working in secret military programs? Or, are these messages being left by extraterrestrial visitors who are trying to display for us the same technology that they use to produce pulsar signals and star shields?

An ETI Connection?

There have been many cases where unconventional flying objects have been sighted either at the time crop circles were being formed or just prior to their appearance. In none of the documented cases has anyone seen or met the occupants of these vehicles, so we cannot be certain whether they are from here or from out there.

Nevertheless given that these vehicles utilize a very advanced method of propulsion that could be used for flight beyond the Earth's atmosphere, the idea that they may be piloted by extraterrestrials remains a very real possibility.

Delgado and Andrews recount one incident that took place in England over Silbury Hill.[22] A woman was driving home late one night in July of 1988 when she noticed a large, golden, disc-shaped object hovering within the cloud cover. A bright parallel beam of white light projected downward from the disc at roughly a 65° angle to a spot a few kilometers away. While she was observing this a "surge of energy" passed through her car, at which point half a dozen articles that had been stored in a pocket on her dashboard suddenly rose up and flew backwards onto her lap and onto the passenger seat next to her. One day later, ten crop circles were discovered at about the location where the beam had been directed. Another five circles appeared several days later, and still others were discovered two months later.

Another sighting was made in 1991 by two Japanese boys. Roy Dutton, who recounts their story, writes:

> As the boys watched, a pillar of 'transparent white steam or smoke' [was] generated downwards from beneath the hovering [glowing orange object]. The pillar revolved and grew wider towards the base, 'giving the impression of a trumpet.' When the base came into contact with the grass, a flattened ring was produced, about 30 cm wide. . . Immediately after the [grass was flattened], the 'trumpet' was retracted, and the object shot back into the sky." . . .One of the young men commented that he felt "a warm wind and drops of water on [his] face" as he watched the grass being whirled down. As he stood transfixed, he reported that he simultaneously heard a "low alternating sound" transliterated as "gu-on, gu-on."[23]

Crop circle photographer Steven Alexander has shot a video that shows a luminous sphere meandering over a crop circle days after the circle had been formed. One eye witness who saw the sphere up close said that it was about the size of a basketball. Another researcher Peter Glastonbury witnessed luminous spheres in a crop field near his home in England. He states:

> After fifteen minutes, we heard sounds that were very much like the crackling you hear around your head when taking off a heavy woolen sweater. My daughter and I both saw a small ball of light hovering in the crop. Through binoculars, I could see several small balls orbiting into a central point. It was dipping in and out of the crop. The next day we discovered a formation

exactly where we had heard the crackling sounds and saw the light the night before.[24]

UFO landings in fields have also been found to leave behind circular swirl patterns. These are presumably produced by the saucer's propulsion beam. In Australia, these lay patterns have become called UFO "nests." These usually have a much rougher form than crop circle designs, their edges not being as sharply defined. The vegetation within them exhibits signs of nonchemical withering, and analysis has shown that some of the changes could have been produced by powerful microwave radiation.[25]

NASA scientist Paul Hill has gathered considerable information from numerous UFO sightings suggesting that force field beams are commonly used by UFOs as a method of propulsion.[26] One of the documented UFO encounter cases he reviews took place in Greece near the villages of Digeliotica and Agiou Apostolou.[27,28] One evening in February 1959 people living there reported seeing a luminous disc emitting a humming noise and circling over the two villages for about 10 minutes. Radios failed to operate and the current in one house went dead. The disc flew low over one house and, as it did, the force of its propulsion beam caused the house to shake and its roof tiles to clatter loudly, making its occupant think that there was an earthquake. When the villagers later inspected the house, they found that many of its roof tiles had been displaced and that others were lying on the ground.

We might theorize that in producing its propulsion beam, a UFO spacecraft is projecting downward an intense column of Tesla-type microwave radiation, that is, shock-type microwave emissions that have the ability to exert forces on the material they intercept. As Tesla observed, shock emissions tend to collimate themselves into a beam. However, to further ensure that the beam's energy is not scattered and dissipated once it strikes the ground, the UFO propulsion system might further utilize the technology of phase conjugation. Accordingly, the microwaves reflected back from the ground towards the spacecraft propulsion apparatus would enter a mixer chamber which would generate an outgoing *phase conjugate* beam of the ground reflected "probe" beam, the two counterpropagating beams being locked together in phase with one another. Consequently, the downward directed phase conjugate microwaves that the spacecraft was emitting, upon reflection, would faithfully return to the spacecraft propulsion apparatus. The spacecraft propulsion apparatus and the Earth's surface, then, would together function as a phase conjugate resonator, allowing microwave radiation to build up within the beam to a very high intensity. The upper end of this resonant column of "solid" radiation would push up against the spacecraft as the lower end pushed down against the Earth's surface, thereby lofting the spacecraft against the Earth's gravitational pull.*

The microwave beam technology that a UFO uses to buoy itself upward may the same one that is being used to form crop circles. UFO sightings indicate that these craft can project several beams at one time and can control not only the direction in which they aim the beams but also the degree to which the beams diverge. By studying the intricate crop circle patterns we can learn something about the sophistication of this propulsion beam technology. The beams would need to have a resolution of the order of just a few millimeters to create crop lay patterns having the kind of sharp-edged boundaries that are observed. Also they would have to be capable not only of pushing but also of pulling, in some cases even uprooting individual stalks. To produce the swirling of the lay patterns, the beam phase conjugator apparatus must be able to induce a vortical component to its beamed force field. The unusually complex weaving and braiding seen in the crop circle patterns suggests that the creators of these designs have very precise and rapid control over their microwave beam "paint brushes."

The 5200 Hz ultrasonic beat frequency that has been detected in one crop circle and the "gu-on, gu-on" sound that was reported to be heard at another sighting would seem to suggest that the crop circle makers produce beams that contain many microwave frequencies whose difference frequencies produce harmonics in the sonic or ultrasonic range. Moreover by properly phasing these various frequencies relative to one another, the beam generator could be made to control the waveform shape of these summed waves and hence the intensity of the force that they generate. By using two or more beam generators, it should be possible to employ conventional

---

* Research carried out by James Woodward, a professor of physics at Cal State Fullerton, indicates that electromagnetic waves can induce lofting forces in piezoelectric ceramic media. His ideas are described in a 1994 U.S. patent (No. 5,280,864) and in a physics journal article (*Foundations of Physics Letters*, vol. 3(5), 1990). Woodward has conducted experiments that confirm this thrust effect in the audio frequency range (~10,000 Hertz), and his calculations suggest that this thrust may be substantially increased at higher frequencies, with optimal performance being obtained in the microwave range (0.1 to 10 gigahertz).

microwave interferometry techniques to laterally order the intensity and direction of these forces across the diameter of a crop circle pattern.

The same force field projection technology that is used for UFO propulsion and crop circle making, and that also appears to be used in highly secret military projects for producing aerial fireball weapons, may be the same technology that extraterrestrial civilizations are using to produce pulsar signals.

Project Centaur

If such a force field technology were possible and could be used for interstellar communication, it might also be used as a means of deflecting superwave cosmic rays so that they would pass harmlessly around a star and its planets. For example, it might be possible, through such field telemetry, to produce a force field "shield" in the direction of the Galactic center to shelter our solar system from an approaching superwave. Deflected from their flight paths by just half of a degree, approaching cosmic rays could be made to miss our solar system and thereby could be prevented from propelling cosmic dust into our interplanetary environment. The shield, however, would need to be huge — over a tenth of a light year in diameter, and would need to be positioned sufficiently far from our solar system, again about one tenth of a light year. Also creating it would require an enormous amount of total energy. But because the shield would function as an energy-storing phase conjugate resonator, the shield's fields could be built up to the required intensity by using a moderate amount of supplied power.

The tubular jet seen to project from the northern side of the Crab supernova remnant (figure 39) may be an example of such a shield being deployed on a much larger scale. In this case the fields would be configured as an immense cylindrical shell measuring 1½ light years in diameter and 2½ light years or more in length. The magnetic forces would be oriented along the length of the cylinder and concentrated at its outer perimeter. Cosmic ray electrons passing through this cylindrical shell would become either captured in spiral orbits within the shell or deflected around the shell.

The Starburst Foundation has advocated that governments who are developing microwave phase conjugate technology for military warfare instead redirect their efforts toward setting up a force field shield for the purposes of planetary defense. The project could be called Project Centaur, named after the Centaurus constellation which depicts a Centaur with raised shield, presumably protecting our solar system from the onslaught of superwave cosmic rays and cosmic dust.*

Many have wondered what is the reason for the continued appearance of crop circles — what have the crop circle makers been trying to communicate to us all these years? If crop circles are being made by visitors from nearby star systems who are members of the Galactic communication network, perhaps they are continuing to create these formations as a way of giving us blatant demonstrations of the technology that we hopefully will one day develop ourselves to protect our planet. By means of the pulsar beacons the Galactic community has been demonstrating this technology from afar. Now, with crop circles it appears we are being shown the use of this technology virtually under our noses.

Contact

There were several reported instances during the twentieth century in which unusual radio or television transmissions had been received from space, some occurring in connection with aerial sightings of unconventional disc shaped flying objects.[29] However, because they were transient events, they could not be later checked and verified, leaving disbelievers unconvinced that signals may have been received from extraterrestrial intelligences. The crop circle phenomenon has the advantage that the "communication," the crop matting patterns, stay around for up to several weeks, long enough to allow many investigators to photograph and study them. Such investigations have developed into a scientific discipline that has become known as "cereology". Still, there are diehard skeptics who refuse to believe people's reports of crop circles forming in a matter of seconds and who have convinced themselves that the hundreds of these designs produced every year in many countries around the world are all the work of a few well-financed pranksters.

The pulsar phenomenon has the advantage that pranksters could not be blamed for creating their signals since it is known that the sources are situated far from our solar system. Like crop circles, pulsars are a persistent phenomenon, although they endure over a

---

* The Starburst Foundation is a nonprofit research institute supported by charitable donations. Information about it may be found at: http://www.etheric.com.

much longer period of time, centuries or millennia, rather than just weeks. As a result, pulsar signals have been diligently studied by many astronomers and the received data has been published in peer reviewed scientific journals, examined, and reexamined. So there is no question that these sources exist. The issue is their *interpretation,* and as history has shown, paradigm shifts do not happen over night. Nevertheless, evidence of an ETI origin for pulsars may be easily checked out by consulting the published data, whose existence and accuracy is well accepted.

Perhaps we have just scratched the surface in our attempt to decipher the messages that pulsars convey. Buried within the rapid shifts in the intensity and polarization direction of their signals may be a wealth of information that is still waiting to be decoded. We should launch a major program that would employ expert crypto- graphers to assess the information content of these transmissions. Perhaps today's SETI researchers might join the effort.

The team of researchers could include remote viewers, people who are able to use their mental powers to "see" events taking place at a far off distance. The viewers might be given the coordinates of certain pulsars and asked to report what information if any they sense coming from those locations. Although there would be no way of directly verifying the validity of what the viewers would be reporting, their perceptions might provide useful guidance to help SETI astronomers locate and later decode intelligible transmissions.

We should not expect all pulsar beacons to be serving as information conduits if, in fact, their main purpose is for spacecraft navigation. But perhaps the Crab pulsar might be good to begin with. Its pulse-to-pulse radio intensity variations are among the largest known for any pulsar.[30] Most of this variability could be intrinsic to the pulsar, in which case it is quite possible that the signal may be conveying intelligible information. Given that the Crab pulsar has been carefully placed on the forefront of the 12,150 B.C. superwave event horizon and at the center of a scale model map of this event horizon, we might surmise that the subject of its transmission has something to do with this superwave event. Curiously, its pulses at high energies contrast with its radio pulses in that their pulse-to-pulse amplitudes remain quite constant. For example, over a seven year period, the amplitude of the Crab pulsar's optical pulses were observed to vary by less than 1 percent.

Other good candidates to study would be long-period pulsars having complex time-averaged pulse profiles. The pulse-to-pulse signal variability has been found to be significantly higher in such pulsars suggesting the possibility that their signal modulation may contain transmitted information.

We may already know enough about the galactic core explosion message of the pulsar network to allow us to devise a return message that would let nearby Galactic civilizations know that we are aware of their transmissions. We could recreate the Crab-Vela pulsar arrow on the ground by situating a pair of Tesla shock wave transmitters at some distance from each other, one pulsing at the rate of the Crab pulsar and the other pulsing at the rate of the Vela pulsar. Nearby extraterrestrial visitors who were members of this Galactic collective should find our transmission of particular interest. Since our transmissions would symbolically be laying out an arrow along the ground, we should be prepared to expect a close encounter or landing somewhere beyond the tip of our "Vela pulsar" transmitter. It would perhaps be prudent to mark out a specific landing site using an array of landing lights.

In effect, we would be creating a contact scenario similar to that portrayed in the movie Close Encounters of the Third Kind. But the motive for doing this would go beyond just the thrill of communicating with visitors from a more advanced civilization. As novices being indoctrinated into the Galactic "federation" our top priority should be to ask them for their knowledge and help to assist our civilization survive the next superwave. We already have been given the invitation to do so.

Appendix A

Galactic Distribution of Pulsars with the Parkes Survey Included

Figure A.1 illustrates how pulsars are distributed with respect to galactic longitude. The data presented here combine the set of pulsars plotted in figure 13 (chapter 2) together with 143 new pulsars, located mostly at southern sky positions and detected in the high-sensitivity Parkes Multibeam survey conducted with the Parkes radio telescope facility in Australia.[1] The new pulsars included here represent about one fourth of the total discovered in the Parkes survey.* Since the Parkes survey is substantially more sensitive than previous pulsar surveys, including it together with previous pulsar data would skew the overall longitudinal distribution by overemphasizing southern galactic longitudes. Hence it was excluded from the data plotted in figure 13.

Nevertheless to view more clearly the distribution of pulsars at southern latitudes, the combined data set is presented in figure A.1, significantly raising the number counts for pulsars lying between longitudes $\ell = 280°$ to $\ell = 20°$. Despite this emphasis of southern longitudes, the northern one-radian pulsar clump still maintains its prominence in the distribution. This combined set fills in the galactic nucleus region to a greater extent than the distribution plotted in figure 13, but the profile is still relatively flat near the Galactic center unlike the centrally humped distribution for supernova remnants.

The southern pulsar clump, with its sharp decline in population at the southern one-radian point ($\ell = 302.65°$), appears more prominent and clearly defined in this plot as compared with figure 13. This feature appears to complement the sharp decline in pulsar population seen at the northern one-radian point ($\ell = 57.24°$). In addition, a significant peak in pulsar population is seen centered at

---

* The remaining Parkes data has not been analyzed and publicly released at the time of writing so it has not been included in figure A.1. The Author sent several emails to the Parkes Survey team requesting the entire raw data set, but received no reply.

Figure A.1. The number of pulsars lying within 5° of the galactic equator plotted as a function of galactic longitude. The left and right arrows indicate longitudes lying one-radian from the Galactic center. This sample includes 143 pulsars detected in the Parkes Multibeam survey.

ℓ = 330° which corresponds to the longitude of the centroid of the North Polar Spur supernova remnant, the closest supernova remnant to the Sun. The outer boundary of the North Polar Spur has begun to envelope our solar neighborhood and bring dust and cometary masses into close proximity with our solar system. This outlying dust has been a key factor responsible for worsening the impact of superwaves on our planet. Propulsion of this material into the solar system during recent superwave passages substantially energized the Sun and induced major changes of the Earth's climate. The presence of this material is likely responsible for the current sequence of ice ages that the Earth has been experiencing over the past million years.[2] Is it just a coincidence that the distribution of pulsars happens to mark out the galactic longitude of the explosion center of this significant supernova remnant?

Appendix B

Ordered Complexity

The following intends to show that pulsar signals not only have a high degree of ordering, but also that there are many types and levels of ordering in their signals. In this way, a case may be built for arguing that pulsars are most likely of artificial origin. The premise here is that highly ordered signal characteristics or the existence of precise cyclical periods would indicate that the source had a high likelihood of being of artificial origin. Such characteristics contrast with most natural astronomical phenomena which as a rule exhibit random modulation of their signals (signal noise) or, if they exhibit cyclical variations, their cycles typically have limited precision. Simply stating that the highly ordered signal characteristics of pulsars is a consequence of the very rare and highly compressed condition of matter found within neutron stars is insufficient reason to abandon consideration of the ETI alternative. For, the neutron star lighthouse model, with its inferred highly ordered emissions, has no independent observational verification. Astronomers have presumed its existence for the express purpose of explaining pulsars as a phenomenon of nature.

The following does not attempt to determine if an intelligible message is being carried in the signal of any one pulsar. It only seeks to establish the high degree of ordered complexity that the signals exhibit and the difficulty that would be encountered in explaining them as arising from naturally occurring sources. Let us now review some of the ordering properties of pulsars.

Pulses and Time-Averaged Pulse Profiles

Pulsar astronomers use the term "subpulse" to refer to the individual radio beeps coming from a pulsar. We will instead continue to use the term "pulse" which should be less confusing to the reader. Pulsar astronomers use this term because they consider the time-averaged profile to be the true pulse feature and the individual pulses forming it as being one step down in the informational hierarchy.

This terminology is undoubtedly influenced by the lighthouse model which interprets the precisely-timed time-averaged profile as the basic datum of neutron star rotation speed.

A given pulse typically lasts for a few thousandths of a second. When its change of intensity, or *amplitude*, is plotted out as a function of time, the resulting trace usually has a hump shape, a simple rise and fall. Furthermore successive pulses typically vary in both intensity and pulse cycle phase. This variation, however, is *nonrandom*. That is, when many pulses are summed up, they collectively produce a highly invariant pulse intensity profile. We refer to this summed profile as the *time-averaged pulse profile*.

The time-averaged pulse profile constitutes a level of informational order situated one hierarchical step above the pulse level. It is built up from pulses in much the same way that a computer image is built up from the series of information bits that compose its image file. The pulses, the pulsar signal's subsidiary information bits, in combination produce an "image" — the time-averaged profile.

Examples of pulse sequences received from each of four pulsars are shown in figures B.1 and B.2. The horizontal time scales shown here are measured in terms of degrees of pulsation cycle phase, rather than in seconds of time, where 360° equals one complete cycle.* Each graph presents a series of 14 consecutive pulse traces. The variously sized ellipses superimposed on the pulse traces denote the intensity and direction of radio signal circular polarization. The open and filled ellipses respectively denote right hand and left hand circular polarization. When superimposed one upon the other, these pulse profiles build up the composite time-averaged pulse profile shown at the top of each graph, a contour that is unique for each pulsar.

While a pulsar's signal intensity, polarization, and arrival time vary considerably from one pulse to the next, the shape of its time-averaged pulse profile remains very constant. Moreover the polarization structure within the envelope of the time-averaged pulse profile — the manner in which the time-averaged pulse polarization varies with pulse cycle phase angle — also remains very constant. The phase position of the time-averaged pulse profile within the pulse cycle is also very constant, as is the length of the pulse cycle.

Over half of the observed pulsars have been found to have pulses

---

* A pulse appearing at a phase of 90° would be displaced from the time reference point by one fourth of the 360° pulse cycle.

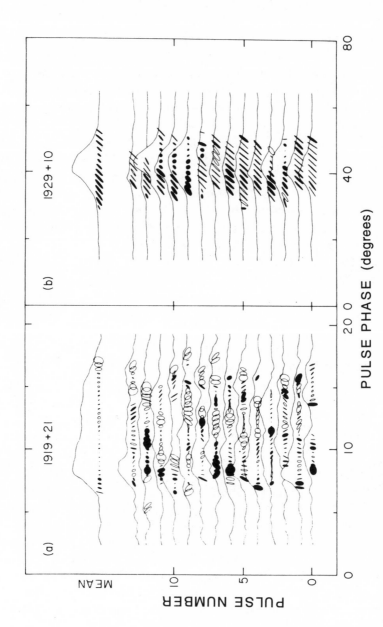

Figure B.1. Pulse sequences and time-averaged pulse profiles for: a) pulsar PSR 1919+21 and b) pulsar PSR 1929+10 (Manchester, Taylor, and Huguenin, *Astrophysical Journal*, figure 14).

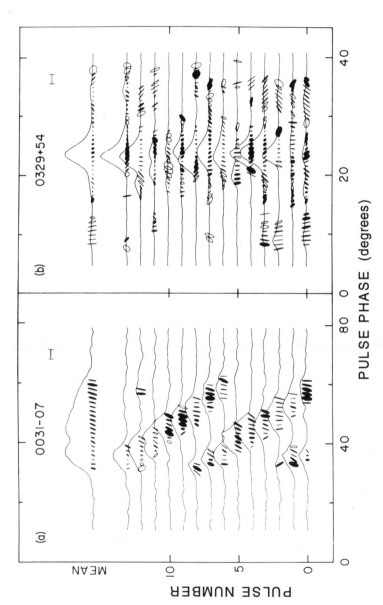

Figure B.2. Pulse sequences and time-averaged pulse profiles for: a) pulsar PSR 0031-07 and b) pulsar PSR 0329+54 (Manchester, Taylor, and Huguenin, *Astrophysical Journal*, figure 1).

Figure B.3. A typical pulse profile for PSR 0950+08 showing
rapid intensity variations (Hankins, *The Astrophysical Journal,* figure 5).

that are themselves composed of a still finer pulsation substructure
that consists of a train of very rapid *micropulses*. Micropulses
typically last a few hundred microseconds. In some cases they
recur with a well-defined periodicity that is distinct from their
pulsar's primary period. The pulses of PSR 2016+28, for example,
are modulated with micropulsations having a recurrence period of
about 900 microseconds. PSR 0950+08 is another example. A
small fraction of its pulses contain micropulse trains with oscillatory
periods ranging from 300 to 700 microseconds, over 1000 times
shorter than the pulsar's primary period which measures about a
quarter of a second. An example of one modulated pulse received
from this pulsar is shown in figure B.3.

Pulse Modulation

In some pulsars, the intensity of a given pulse is seen to correlate
in a specific way with the intensity of pulses that preceded it. For
example, there are pulsars in which the intensity of consecutive
pulses oscillates in a regular fashion, signal strength being observed
to alternately wax and wane over a series of pulses. In other pulsars
this periodic *pulse modulation* is present only when every other pulse
in a sequence is sampled. The period of such a modulation cycle,
customarily designated as P_3, typically ranges from 2 to 20 times the
pulsar's primary period. The primary period, which characterizes
the average time between successive pulses, is designated as P_1.
Compared with the primary period, the pulse modulation period is

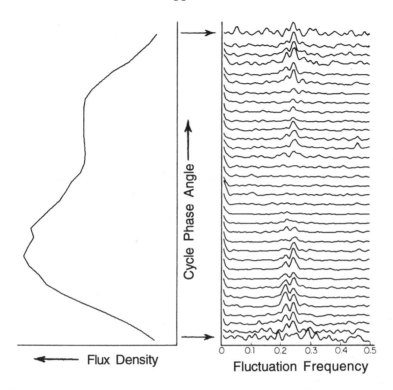

Figure B.4. Left: the time-averaged pulse profile of pulsar PSR 1919+21 showing intensity plotted against cycle phase. Right: fluctuation spectra observed in 34 time channels each corresponding to a phase segment of the time-averaged pulse profile (Backer, *Astrophysical Journal*, figure 1).

far less precise. Even in pulsars having a well-defined pulse modulation pattern, P_3 is precise to no more than two to three decimal places.

Further adding to this complexity, pulse modulation is often found to occur *only at certain phase angle positions in the time-averaged pulse profile*. Consider for example PSR 1919+21, the original pulsar discovered by Jocelyn Bell. The left hand side of figure B.4 displays this pulsar's time-averaged pulse profile, also seen in figure B.1-(a). The profile has been rotated by 90 degrees so that its phase angle axis is plotted here vertically. Furthermore the vertical phase angle axis has been segmented into 34 cycle phase "windows," and the pulse modulation frequencies within each of these phase windows have been separately analyzed. The frequency distribution for each of these windows has then been plotted to form the series of traces to the right. A peak in any of these traces indicates the pulse per second frequency at which pulses recur at that particular phase in the pulse cycle. For example, the lower traces, which correspond to the leading part of the time-averaged profile, show peaks at around 0.21 and 0.24 Hertz, indicating that pulses wax and wane about every 4.2 and 4.8 seconds, or at about 3 times the pulsar's primary period. Further up, the traces indicate no discernible modulation for the middle part of the pulse profile. Still further up, traces corresponding to the trailing part of the pulse profile indicate again strong pulse modulation at similar frequencies, with a hint of a 0.44 Hertz modulation, second harmonic, appearing in just one or two of these traces. This frequency versus phase analysis forms a personality fingerprint of this pulsar's pulse profile which amazingly does not change over extended periods of observation. It is such ordering complexity that leads us to ask whether pulsar signals may be of artificial origin.

Pulse Drifting

One of the most unusual ordering phenomena observed in pulsars is that of *pulse drifting*. In pulse drifting, each successive pulse is slightly displaced in phase, giving the appearance that over time the pulse gradually moves across the time-averaged pulse profile. One example of this is shown in figure B.2-(a). Usually pulses drift from right to left, that is, from the trailing portion to the leading portion of the time-averaged pulse profile. However, in some pulsars the reverse drift direction is also observed. As a pulse approaches the leading edge of the profile, it weakens and vanishes within a few pulse periods. Meanwhile, a new pulse arises near the trailing edge of the profile to continue the drifting process. The pulses repeatedly scan across the time-averaged pulse profile with a characteristic period P_3, equal to the pulse modulation period described earlier. Moreover in some pulse cycles, the leading and trailing pulses will both appear together, separated by a characteristic time interval which usually is designated as P_2. This pulse spacing interval is yet another invariant feature observed in pulsars.

Each pulsar that exhibits pulse drifting has its own unique variety of drift activity. It is worthwhile describing here in some detail these variations to show that pulsar signals can have a remarkable variety of extremely complex ordering modes.

Linear Drifters. Some pulsars are classified as *linear drifters* because consecutive pulses drift across the time-averaged pulse profile at a constant rate. So, when successive pulse cycles are mapped out, consecutive pulses form a series of straight diagonal lines, like those seen figure B.2-(a). In this particular pulsar, PSR 0031-07, successive sequences of drifting pulses maintain similar drift rates. However, there are other linear drifters in which each successive drift sequence maintains a drift rate different from the preceding sequence, with no particular pattern being apparent in the evolution from one drift rate to the next. When the pulse sequences from such a pulsar are mapped out, they form a series of diagonal strings, each having a different slope. PSR 2016+28, whose time-averaged pulse profile is composed of two components, exhibits the additional peculiarity that linear pulse drifting tends to occur more frequently in one component than in the other.

Nonlinear Drifters. In certain other pulsars the pulses progressively change their drift rate as they scan across the time-averaged pulse profile. These types of pulsars have been classified as *nonlinear drifters*. For example, in PSR 1919+21 pulses drift rapidly into the pulse profile envelope from the profile's trailing edge, decelerate as they pass the center of the pulse profile, and accelerate as they drift out at the profile's leading edge. Thus each pulse drift sequence executes an S-shaped trajectory when consecutive pulse cycles are plotted out next to one another.

Nonrandom Pulse Patterns. Finally, some pulsars have such complex pulse sequences that it is not possible to trace their pulse drift paths. Yet definite patterns of pulse recurrence are detectable. In PSR 1133+16, for example, brief intervals in the data sequence are discernible in which pulse patterns composed of three to six consecutive pulses occasionally recur. These patterns consist variously of single pulses that appear in either of the two pulse profile components, pulses that appear in both components, and null pulses — pulses that fail to occur.

PSR 0329+54 is another pulsar that exhibits nonrandomly patterned pulses. When a strong pulse appears in component-1 of its four-component pulse profile, this event is generally preceded in component-3 by several weak or missing pulses and followed by strong pulses. Also when pulses appear in component-4, they are often accompanied by pulses in component-3 and followed one period later by a strong pulse in component-3.[1] The complexity of this organized behavior begins to approach that found in simple computer logic circuits.

Both pulse drifting and pulse sequence patterning are very unusual ordering phenomena that present a severe challenge to theoreticians seeking natural explanations for pulsars. Although possible natural causes have been suggested for this ordering in individual pulsars, astronomers are far from having a successful self-consistent theory that explains all types of pulse ordering. Such varied and complex signal ordering, however, might be expected if pulsars are beacons of ETI origin, their creators making extraordinary efforts to ensure that their signals are not misinterpreted as being of natural origin.

Multi-component Correlated Drifting. In most pulsars, the time-averaged pulse profile spans a small portion of the total pulse cycle. However, in pulsar PSR 0826-34 *the profile stretches over the entire pulsation cycle*. It is one of the few pulsars known to have such a broad pulse profile in the radio spectral region. Its broad 3-component profile allows it to accommodate five, or on occasion six, well-defined bands of linearly drifting pulses, *all of which drift across the time-averaged pulse profile in sync with one another*.[2] This pulsar is unique in that no other pulsar has so many bands of drifting pulses. Pulse drifting spanning 45% of the entire pulse cycle. In no other pulsar does pulse drifting occur over such a large part of the pulse cycle.

In most pulsars that exhibit pulse drifting, pulses normally drift in one direction, usually from the trailing to leading edge of the pulse profile. However, in PSR 0826-34, the pulses drift first in one direction, stop, and then drift back in the *reverse* direction, changing their direction at irregular intervals. All the while they stay in march step with one another. This drift reversal phenomenon has been observed only in this pulsar to date. Another unusual feature is that the pulse drift rate progressively increases with each successive pulse cycle until the drift rate reverses at which it progressively slows down from its initially high drift rate.

Furthermore as these pulses drift, they are kept spaced from one another by a fixed time interval, equal to 8% of the primary pulse period ($P_2 \sim 0.081\ P_1$, or 0.15 seconds). In any given pulse cycle, 5, or sometimes 6, pulses will appear, each spaced from one another by this fixed P_2 interval, *regardless of how fast the pulses happen to be drifting*.

Yet another unusual feature of this pulsar is that its pulse transmissions experience long interruptions called *pulse nulling*. These blank intervals have varied lengths, ranging from several seconds to over seven hours. Although pulse nulling has been observed in a few other pulsars, PSR 0826-34 is unusual in that it stays in its nulling state for at least 70 percent of the time. As in other nulling pulsars, the phase positions of the pulses *freeze* during the nulling period, but this pulsar is unique in that the phase positions of all five or six bands of drifting pulses become frozen.

Observations of just this one pulsar shook the foundations of pulsar theory, sending all previous versions of the lighthouse model to the trash can. Previously, pulse drifting had been explained by supposing that individual pulses were produced by cosmic ray particle cascades, or "sparks," that precessed around the star's magnetic pole as a result of the pole's magnetic field acting on electric fields in the cascade; the stronger the magnetic field, the greater the drift rate. However, such models predict that pulse drifting should proceed at a constant rate and only in one direction.[3] To instead account for the observed continually changing drift rates and sudden reversals of drift direction, the lighthouse model is left to the absurd prediction that the neutron star's magnetic field axis must progressively change its orientation relative to the star's spin axis and that at times it negotiates radical flips. Moreover, we are asked to believe that, in engaging in these gymnastics, this powerful field, which is a trillion times stronger than the Earth's magnetic field, for some reason does not alter the even-spaced timing of these precessing particle cascades. Furthermore the lighthouse model fails to explain why the pulsar's entire emission process mysteriously shuts down for periods of up to seven hours or more and somehow *remembers* the cycle phase at which its drifting stopped prior to the time its emission shut down!

In reporting this pulsar's unusual behavior, pulsar astronomers J. Biggs, Peter McCulloch, P. Hamilton, Richard Manchester, and Andrew Lyne conclude:*

> Current proposals for the drifting subpulse mechanism do not adequately describe the observed drifting subpulse behavior.[4]

A viable lighthouse model must be able to explain the variable drift rates with drift reversals, the correlation of the multiple drift bands, the constancy of the P_2 pulse spacing, the extended pulse nulling, the pulse "freezing" that remembers the pre-null pulse phase, and the observation that radio continuum is transmitted during

---

* The term "subpulse" used in the quote below signifies "pulse" according to the terminology that is adopted here in this book.

the entire pulse cycle. However, such a model runs the risk of being unusually complicated and contrived. J. Biggs and his colleagues have sketched out a way in which the lighthouse model might be modified to account for a few of these unexplained properties — the correlated pulse drifting and drift reversal pheno mena. They suggest the possibility that the neutron star's pulse emission intensity is *modulated by two phase-drifting standing wave field patterns that reside near the star's surface* and whose modulating effects interfere with one another so as to create the observed pulsar signal behavior. They presume that these standing waves are somehow generated naturally and that they rotate along with the neutron star without being disrupted.

Although it is not clear whether a hypothetical neutron star would be able to pull this off, it is interesting to note how close their model comes to the stationary-beam ETI beacon model described at the end of chapter 7. The only differences are the following: a) in the ETI model these modulating standing wave fields are engineered rather than produced by nature, b) these fields do not rotate with the star, but are artificially projected near the star's surface, and c) the star is a white-dwarf-sized X-ray star, rather than a neutron star.

Interestingly, this unusual pulsar is the Vela pulsar's nearest pulsar neighbor. The two are separated by only 11 degrees of arc and lie about the same distance from the Sun, PSR 0826-34 lying only 4 percent further away. Their placement relative to one another shows no particularly significant alignment as was observed between the Crab pulsar and PSR 0525+21. But this coincidence is worth noting.

Mode Switching

As described in chapter 7, mode switching is one of the most perplexing properties of pulsars. Pulsars that exhibit this behavior have more than one stable pulsation mode, each with its own time-averaged pulse profile and unique pulse modulation characteristics. Such pulsars will suddenly switch from one mode to another without showing any change in either their primary period or period derivative. As of the time of writing, 7 pulsars have been identified as mode switchers, two others being possible additional candidates.

One interesting mode switcher, PSR 1237+25, exhibits two stable modes, each having five components to its time-averaged pulse profile (figure B.5). The two modes are designated as "*normal*" and

Figure B.5. Intensity and polarization properties of the time-averaged pulse profile for PSR 1237+25 observed at a radio frequency of 430 megahertz. Normal mode: solid line; abnormal mode: dashed line (Bartel et al., *The Astrophysical Journal*, figure 7).

"*abnormal*". The pulsar usually transmits in the normal mode, but about every few hours it flips into its abnormal mode and stays there for several minutes before flipping back. When pulsing in its normal mode, the pulsar exhibits very unusual pulse ordering behavior. Pulses alternately emerge in component-1 and component-5 of its five-component time-averaged profile, pulses reappearing in each component with a characteristic period P_3 of 2.7 seconds equal to about twice the pulsar's primary period of 1.382449 seconds. But what is even more unusual, pulses emerging in component-1 are observed to subsequently split into two separate pulse trains that drift in opposite directions, one toward the leading edge of the component and the other toward the trailing edge. When the pulsar switches to its abnormal mode, this unusually complex correlated multi-component modulation almost totally disappears. Upon returning to the normal mode, the periodic behavior is faithfully remembered and resumed. Such intricate signal ordering gives very good reason to consider that these transmissions may have an ETI origin.

Another mode switcher, PSR 0329+54, exhibits as many as three abnormal modes in addition to its normal mode! Moreover, this pulsar has differing numbers of abnormal modes available to it depending on the particular radio frequency that the pulsar is viewed at. As seen in figure B.6, abnormal mode A is present at frequencies of 0.41 gigahertz and from 5 to 14.8 gigahertz; abnormal mode B appears at a frequency of 0.83 gigahertz; both abnormal modes A and B are detected at 2.7 gigahertz; and finally all three abnormal modes are present at 1.4 gigahertz. As mentioned in chapter 7, we are led to question whether it is just a coincidence that all three switching modes are present at the 1.4 gigahertz neutral-hydrogen emission frequency which SETI astronomers deem to be the most likely frequency to be used in narrow band ETI radio communication.

PSR 1822-09 is another quite unique mode-switching pulsar. About every five minutes, it switches between a quiescent mode (Q mode) and a burst mode (B mode); see figure B.7. The quiescent mode is characterized by a single-component main pulse followed about half a pulsation cycle later by a weak interpulse (not shown in the diagram). When the pulsar switches to its burst mode, the main peak almost doubles its intensity and is accompanied by a new "precursor peak" of lesser intensity. Astronomers have discovered that during the quiescent mode, pulses in the interpulse and main pulse are correlated, implying that the emission processes in the two

Figure B.6. Time-averaged pulse profiles for PSR 0329+54 at each of eight different frequencies. The normal mode is shown as a solid line. The three abnormal modes, designated as A, B, and C, are shown as dashed and dotted lines (Bartel et al., *Astrophysical Journal*, figure 3).

Figure B.7. Quiescent and burst mode mean profiles for the main pulse component of PSR 1822-09 at 1.62 gigahertz (Fowler et al., *Astronomy and Astrophysics*, figure 3).

peaks are causally linked. However, contrary to expectation, when the pulsar switches to its burst mode, the interpulse does not increase in intensity like the main pulse, but instead vanishes below the threshold of detection! This paradox poses quite a problem to theoreticians who seek a logical natural cause for this unusual behavior. Such paradoxical behavior, though, would be quite plausible if this mode of behavior were one of many techniques used by extraterrestrials to foil our attempts to pass off their message as a natural phenomenon.

The quiescent and burst modes of this pulsar also exhibit very different pulse drifting behavior. When the pulsar is in its quiescent mode, pulses drift from the leading to trailing edge of its main peak with a relatively well-defined period P_3 equal to about 40 times the pulsar's primary period. The drift rate varies such that the pulses accelerate as they approach the center of the main pulse profile and then decelerate as they approach the profile's trailing edge. When the pulsar switches to the burst mode, pulse drifting in the main pulse ceases, but appears sporadically 5 to 10 percent of the time in the precursor pulse with a period equal to 11 times the primary period.

Mode Switching with Pulse Quantization. Another interesting pulsar, PSR 0031-07, exhibits mode switching among three modes:

A, B, and C, each exhibiting pulse drifting behavior and each with its own unique drift rate. The drift rates for modes A, B, and C are respectively 1.7 ± 0.2, 3.2 ± 0.6, and 5.3 ± 1.1 degrees of phase per primary pulse period, suggesting a quantized ratio relationship of 1 to 2 to 3. So these pulses are not only ordered so that they drift in phase in a regular manner, but also this drifting process, in turn, is ordered to allow only drifting rates that bear a certain integer relation to one another. Moreover despite these three different pulse drifting speeds (three different profile scan periods, P_3), in all three modes the interval between successive pulses, period P_2, stays fixed at a value equal to 6 percent of the pulsar's primary period. While these ordered relationships make little sense from the standpoint of contemplating a possible natural cause, it would be quite plausible if this pulsar, like many others, is an extraterrestrial communication beacon.

Mode Switching with Pulse Nulling. Besides these complexities, PSR 0031-07 exhibits unusual interruptions in its pulsed emissions (see figure B.8). Rather than transmitting a steady train of pulses, it emits bursts of pulses consisting of several dozens to as many as 100 pulses. These bursts are separated by blank intervals of varied lengths made up of null pulses that are at least a hundred fold weaker than the burst mode pulses and often are totally undetectable. Null intervals may span anywhere from a few to as many as 100 or more pulse periods. Most bursts from this pulsar begin abruptly with a pair of high-intensity pulses, one positioned close to the leading edge of the time-averaged pulse profile and the other positioned close to its trailing edge. The pulses that follow then go on to drift toward the envelope's leading edge at the characteristic drift rate of the mode that the pulsar happens to be switched to at that time.

Mode Switching with Pulse Grammar. About 80 percent of the bursts from PSR 0031-07 are dominated entirely by Mode B pulse drifting. The remaining 20 percent have been the subject of considerable interest. They consist of two drifting modes that occur consecutively, either A followed by B, or B followed by C. In such bursts, the pulsar might make several pulse scans across the time-averaged pulse profile at one mode (e.g., A) and then, right in the middle of the burst, suddenly switch to an alternate mode with a different pulse drift rate (e.g., B); see figure B.9. About three fourths of these dual mode bursts are composed of A and B mode sequences and about one fourth are composed of B and C mode

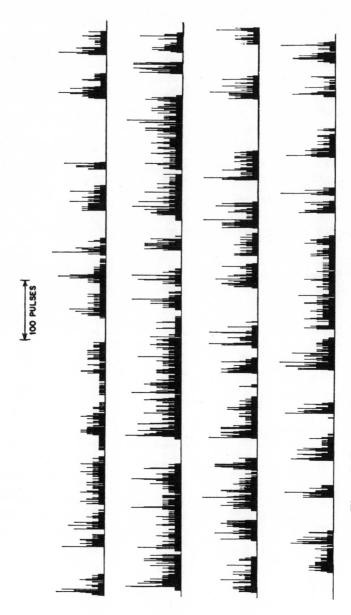

Figure B.8. A continuous record of 3800 pulses from pulsar PSR 0031–07 (Huguenin et al., *Astrophysical Journal*, figure 1).

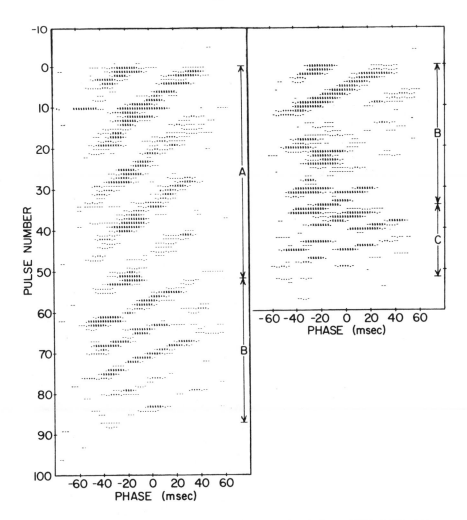

Figure B.9. A succession of pulses received from PSR 0031-07 showing linearly drifting pulse trains. The three drift modes are marked in the right margin as A, B, and C (adapted from Huguenin et al., *The Astrophysical Journal*, figure 4).

sequences. A and C modes *never occur together in the same burst; nor do they occur alone like B mode bursts*. Thus not only are pulse drift rates quantized in this pulsar, but the process of switching from one quantized drift rate to another also appears to be highly structured, being governed by a kind of *pulse mode grammar*.

Mode Switching with Pulse Phase Memory. PSR 0031-07 exhibits yet another ordering effect. During a nulling period, it somehow "remembers" the phase positions that its pulses had at the time its emission shut off so that, when the pulsar turns on again with a new burst, its pulses have not moved appreciably from their former phase positions. It is as if pulse drifting "freezes" while nulling is in progress, and then recommences when nulling ends. Careful studies of two single mode pulsars that exhibit pulse nulling (PSR 0809+74 and PSR 0818-13) indicate that pulses are present during nulls, although at very low intensity. In this case, the pulse drifting does not freeze, but continues to drift, although at a very reduced rate.[5] Consequently, this type of nulling could be classified as a kind of mode switching phenomenon.

Mode Switching with Mode Memory. The mode switching pulsar PSR 2319+60 also emits its pulses in bursts separated by null periods that occur about 30% of the time.[6] It has three modes designated as A, B, and Abn (an abnormal mode), each of which is characterized by a different pulse drift rate. Like PSR 0031-07, its process of switching from one mode to another is governed by rules. During a burst, mode switching is allowed to occur either as $A \rightarrow B$, $B \rightarrow Abn$, or $A \rightarrow B \rightarrow Abn$. No reverse transitions have been observed, such as $B \rightarrow A$ or $A \rightarrow Abn$. Moreover the mode transition rules often appear to span null periods. For example, the forward transition, $A \rightarrow null \rightarrow B$, occurs much more frequently than the reverse, $B \rightarrow null \rightarrow A$. It is as if this mode switching pulsar remembers what mode it was in before the null period began (e.g., mode A) so that it can adopt an allowed mode after the null period ends (e.g., mode B).

The various types of complex signal ordering reviewed above would be the kind of thing we might expect if pulsars have been fabricated by intelligent beings. Such varied kinds of signal ordering could be their attempt to convince us that pulsars are indeed artifactual beacons.

Appendix C

Particle Beam Communicator Luminosity

The radio luminosity coming from the "low-tech" particle beam communicator described in chapter 7 may be calculated using the following equation:

$$L = 4\pi d^2 \, (W/P_1) \, (S/8\gamma^3) \, \Delta v, \tag{1}$$

where d is the distance of the source from the Earth, W is the pulse width at half maximum intensity, P_1 is the primary pulse period, S is the radiation flux density of the source at a given frequency as seen by an Earth observer, γ is the Lorentz factor of the radiating electrons due to their relativistic velocity v (i.e., $\gamma = 1/\sqrt{1 - v^2/c^2}$, and Δv is the band width under consideration. The quantity $1/8\gamma^3$ in the above equation is the factor by which we must reduce S, the observed radiation flux density, to obtain the actual radiation flux density of the source to adjust for relativistic beaming.

This example assumes that the electrons in the communicator's particle beam have a kinetic energy of 50 billion electron volts, which is equivalent to a Lorentz factor of $\gamma = 2 \times 10^5$. Also suppose that $S = 8 \times 10^{-24}$ ergs/second/centimeter^2/Hertz at a frequency of 400 megahertz; which is equivalent to the flux density observed from the Crab pulsar. Also let d = 6600 light years = 6.6×10^{21} centimeters, the distance to the Crab pulsar, and let W/P = 0.42, the width-to-pulse-period ratio for the Crab pulsar. For a bandwidth of Δv = 400 megahertz, relation (1) predicts a luminosity of 10^{13} ergs/sec = one megawatt. By comparison the 20 trillion electron volt superconducting supercollider which the U.S. had planned to build was expected to achieve a particle power flux 300 times this amount.

This estimates just the energy stored in the electron beam. The actual power drawn by the accelerator to achieve this electron energy flux will be substantially greater. With a one percent acceleration efficiency, the total power requirement amounts to 100 megawatts, the amount supplied by a small nuclear power plant.

The Crab pulsar is one of the few that emits pulses at optical, X-ray, and gamma ray energies. In fact, in this high energy portion of the electromagnetic spectrum it radiates 10^4 to 10^5 times the amount of energy that it emits in the radio region of its spectrum. These higher luminosities could be attained by accelerating the beam's electrons to 2 trillion electron volts ($\gamma = 8 \times 10^6$).

Notes

1 The Pulsar Enigma

1. W. Sullivan, *Black Holes* (Garden City, NY: Anchor Press, 1979), p. 123.

2. A. Hewish, S. J. Bell, J. D. H. Pilkington, P. F. Scott, and R. A. Collins, "Observation of a rapidly pulsating radio source." *Nature* 217 (1968): 709-713.

3. *New York Post*, as cited in Collyns, R. *Did Spacemen colonize the Earth?* (London: Pelham Books, 1974), p. 231.

4. R. Jastrow and M. H. Thompson, *Astronomy: Fundamentals and Frontiers* (New York: John Wiley & Sons, 1977), p. 198.

5. T. Gold, "Rotating neutron stars as the origin of the pulsating radio sources." *Nature* 218 (1968): 731-732.

6. C. Misner, K. Thorne, and J. A. Wheeler, *Gravitation* (San Francisco: Freeman and Co., 1973), p. 628.

7. Winnipeg Free Press, November 27, 1974.

2 A Galactic Message

1. P. A. LaViolette, "Evidence that radio pulsars may be artificial beacons of ETI origin." 195th American Astronomical Society meeting, Atlanta, GA, January 2000.

2. Pulsar data is taken from: ftp://pulsar.princeton.edu/pub/catalog/.

3. D. H. Clark, and J. L. Caswell, "A study of Galactic supernova remnants based on Molonglo-Parkes observational data." *Monthly Notices of the Royal Astronomical Society* 174 (1996): 267-305, fig. 8.

4. S. Johnston, "Evidence for a deficit of pulsars in the inner Galaxy." *Monthly Notices of Royal Astronomical Society* 268 (1994): 595-601.

5. M. Alcubierre, "The warp drive: Hyperfast travel within general relativity" *Classic and Quantum Gravity* 11 (1994): L73.

6. H. Puthoff, "SETI, the velocity-of-light limitation, and the Alcubierre warp drive: An integrating overview." *Physics Essays* 9 (1996): 156.

7. T. T. Brown, "How I control gravity." *Science and Invention magazine*, August 1929.

8. P. A. LaViolette, *Subquantum Kinetics: The Alchemy of Creation* (Alexandria, VA: Starlane Publications, 1994), ch. 9.

9. P. Cornille, "Review of the application of Newton's third law in physics." *Progress in Energy and Combustion Science* 25 (1999): 161-210.

10. Gravity Research Group, "Electrogravitics Systems: An examination of electrostatic motion, dynamic counterbary, and barycentric

control." Report GRG 013/56, London: Aviation Studies (International) Ltd., Special Weapons Study Unit, February 1956. (Declassified report: Wright Patterson Air Force Base ID number 3-1401-00034-5879.)

11. P. A. LaViolette, "The U.S. Antigravity Squadron." in *Electrogravitics Systems: Reports on a New Propulsion Methodology*, ed. T. Valone (Washington, D.C.: Integrity Research Institute, 1994).

12. P. A. LaViolette, "An introduction to subquantum kinetics." *International Journal of General Systems* 11 (1985): 281-345.

13. LaViolette, *Subquantum Kinetics*.

14. T. K. Ishii, and G. C. Giakos, "Radio Messages Faster Than Light." *Microwaves & RF* 30, Aug. 1991, pp 114–119.

15. T. K. Ishii and G. C. Giakos, "Rapid Pulsed Microwave Propagation." *IEEE Microwave & Guided Wave Letters* 1(12), Dec. 1991, pp 374-375

16. A. Enders and G. Nimtz, "On superluminal barrier traversal." *Physical Review* E 48 (1993): 632.

17. N. Hawkes, "Going faster than light." *The London Times*, April 3, 1995, p. 14.

18. W. M. Cady, "An investigation relative to Thomas Townsend Brown." Office of Naval Research, Pasadena, June 1952, p. 1.

19. T. T. Brown, "Electrogravitational Communication System." patent disclosure, September 1953; available at http://www.soteria.com.

20. Intel, "Towards flight without stress or strain... or weight." *Interavia* ll(5) (1956): 373-374.

21. J. Dea, "Instantaneous interactions." Proceedings of the 1986 International Tesla Symposium, Colorado Springs, CO: International Tesla Society, 1986, p. 4-39.

3 One-Radian Marker Beacons

1. D. Backer et al., "A millisecond pulsar." *Nature* 300 (1982): 615-618.

2. "Newly discovered pulsar is 20 times faster than Crab pulsar." *Physics Today*, March 1983, pp. 19-21.

3. J. H. Taylor, R. Manchester, and A. Lyne, "Catalog of 558 pulsars." *Astrophysical Journal Supplement Series* 88 (1993): 529-568.

4. A. S. Fruchter, D. R. Stinebring, and J. H. Taylor, "A millisecond pulsar in an eclipsing binary." *Nature* 333 (1988): 237-239.

5. R. Preston, "The eclipsing death star." *Discovery*, Aug. 1988, pp. 41-46.

4 The Galactic Imperative

1. P. A. LaViolette, *Earth Under Fire: Humanity's Survival of the Apocalypse* (Alexandria, VA: Starlane Publications, 1997).

2. P. A. LaViolette, *Beyond the Big Bang: Ancient Myth and the Science of Continuous Creation* (Rochester, Vermont: Park Street Press, 1995).

3. Ibid.

4. P. A. LaViolette, "Galactic explosions, cosmic dust invasions, and climatic change." Ph.D. dissertation, Portland State Univ., 1983.

5. P. A. LaViolette, "Cosmic-ray volleys from the Galactic center and their recent impact on the Earth environment." *Earth Moon Planets* 37 (1987): 241-286.

6. G. C. Bower, H. Falcke, and D. C. Backer, "Circular polarization in Sagittarius A*." 195th American Astronomical Society meeting, Atlanta, GA, January 2000.

7. LaViolette, Ph.D. dissertation, ch. 3.

8. Ibid., ch. 4, 5.

9. LaViolette, *Earth Under Fire*, ch. 3, 10.

10. P. A. LaViolette, "Global warming at the Termination I boundary: Part II. An extraterrestrial cause." 1999 (submitted for journal publication).

11. H. A. Zook, J. B. Hartung, and D. Storzer, "Solar flare activity: Evidence for large-scale changes in the past." *Icarus* 32 (1977): 106-126.

12. T. Gold, "Apollo II observations of a remarkable glazing phenomenon on the lunar surface." *Science* 165 (1969): 1345-1349.

13. B. S. Boeckl, "A depth profile of ^{14}C in the lunar rock 12002." *Earth and Planetary Science Letters* 16 (1972): 269-272.

14. P. A. LaViolette, "Global warming at the Termination I boundary: Part I. Supporting evidence and the inadequacy of terrestrial climate change mechanisms." 1999 (submitted for journal publication).

15. K. A. Hughen et al., "Deglacial changes in ocean circulation from an extended radiocarbon calibration." *Nature* 391 (1998): 65-68.

16. LaViolette, *Earth Under Fire*, ch. 7.

17. LaViolette, "Global Warming at the Termination I Boundary: Part II."

18. LaViolette, Ph.D. dissertation, ch. 4, 5.

19. LaViolette, *Earth Under Fire*, ch. 3, 10.

20. Ibid., ch. 1.

21. LaViolette, *Beyond the Big Bang*, ch. 9.

22. R. L. Thompson, *Alien Identities: Ancient Insights into Modern UFO Phenomena* (San Diego, CA: Govardhan Hill Publishing, 1993).

23. Plutarch, "Lucullus." in *Plutarch's Lives* vol. 2, (Cambridge, MA: Harvard University Press, 1968), pp. 495-497.

5 Superwave Warning Beacons

1. W. H. Tucker, "Supernova in the sail." *Star and Sky* 2(1) (1980): 36.

2. G. Michanowsky, *The Once and Future Star* (New York: Barnes and Noble, 1979).

3. P. A. LaViolette, *Earth Under Fire: Humanity's Survival of the Apocalypse* (Alexandria, VA: Starlane Publications, 1997), ch. 7.

4. J. H. Taylor, and D. R. Stinebring, "Recent progress in the understanding of pulsars." *Annual Reviews of Astronomy and Astrophysics* 24 (1986): 303.

5. H. Ögelman, L. Koch-Miramond, and M. Auriére, "Measurement of the Vela pulsar's proper motion and detection of the optical counterpart of its compact X-ray nebula." *Astrophysical Journal* 342 (1989): L83–L86.

6. G. F. Bignami and P. A. Caraveo, "On the birthplace of PSR 0833-45: Or, is the Vela pulsar associated with the Vela SNR?" *The Astrophysical Journal* 325 (1988): L5-L7.

7. V. Trimble, "Motions and Structure of the Filamentary Envelope of the Crab Nebula." *Astronomical Journal* 73 (1968): 535-547.

8. J. H. Taylor, R. N. Manchester, and A. G. Lyne, "Catalog of 558 pulsars." *Astrophysical Journal Supplement Series* 88 (1993): 553.

9. R. Isaacman, "NP0532 and a hole in the Crab Nebula." *Nature* 268 (1977): 317-318.

10. P. A. LaViolette, Galactic Explosions, Cosmic Dust Invasions and Climatic Change, Ph.D. dissertation, Portland State Univ., 1983, ch. 5.

11. LaViolette, *Earth Under Fire*, pp. 287-288.

12. LaViolette, Ph.D. dissertation, ch. 5.

13. P. A. LaViolette, *Subquantum Kinetics: The Alchemy of Creation* (Alexandria, VA: Starlane Publications, 1994), pp. 145-148.

14. P. A. LaViolette, "The planetary-stellar mass-luminosity relation: Possible evidence of energy nonconservation?" *Physics Essays* 5 (4) (1992): 536-544.

15. W. C. Erickson et al., "Very long baseline interferometer observations of Taurus A and other sources at 121.6 MHz." *Astrophysical Journal* 177 (1972): 101.

16. LaViolette, Ph.D. dissertation, ch. 5.

17. LaViolette, *Earth Under Fire*, p. 282.

18. Ibid., p. 287.

19. LaViolette, Ph.D. dissertation, ch. 5.

20. G. D. Schmidt, J. Angel, and E. Beaver, "The small-scale polarization of the Crab Nebula." *Astrophysical Journal* 227 (1979): 106-113.

21. W. J. Cocke, M. Disney, G. Muncaster, and T. Gehrels, "Optical polarization of the Crab Nebula pulsar." *Nature* 227 (1970): 1327-1329.

22. LaViolette, Ph.D. dissertation, ch. 5.

23. P. A. LaViolette, "Cosmic-ray volleys from the Galactic center and their recent impact on the Earth environment." *Earth Moon Planets* 37 (1987): 241-286.

24. LaViolette, *Earth Under Fire*, p. 283.

25. S. P. Reynolds and D. C. Ellison, "Electron acceleration in Tycho's and Kepler's supernova remnants: Spectral evidence of Fermi shock acceleration." *The Astrophysical Journal* 399 (1992): L75-L78.

26. C. Heiles, D. B. Campbell, and J. M. Rankin, "Pulsar NP 0532: Properties and systematic polarization of individual strong pulses at 430 MHz." *Nature* 226 (1970): 529-531.

27. A. G. Lyne, R. S. Pritchard, F. Graham-smith, and F. Camilo, "Very low braking index for the Vela pulsar." *Nature* 381 (1996): 497-498.

28. A. G. Lyne and F. Graham-Smith, *Pulsar Astronomy* (London: Cambridge University Press, 1998), p. 63.

29. C. L. Bhat, M. L. Sapru, and C. L. Kaul, "A nonrandom component in cosmic rays of energy greater than or equal to 10 to the 14th ev." *Nature* 288 (1980): 146-149.

6 Sky Maps of a Celestial Disaster

1. P. A. LaViolette, "Galactic explosions, cosmic dust invasions, and climatic change." Ph.D. dissertation, Portland State Univ., 1983, pp. 291, 304.

2. P. A. LaViolette, *Earth Under Fire: Humanity's Survival of the Apocalypse* (Alexandria, VA: Starlane Publications, 1997).

3. Ibid., pp. 36-39.

4. Ibid., pp. 61-66.

5. Ibid., ch. 2.

6. Ibid., pp. 76-88.

7. S. de Lubicz, Sacred Science (Rochester, VT: Inner Traditions, 1961, 1982, p. 174.

8. LaViolette, *Earth Under Fire*, pp. 160, 171-172.

9. LaViolette, *Earth Under Fire*, pp. 235-238.

10. T. R. Gull, and R. A. Fesen, "Deep optical imagery of the Crab Nebula's jet." *The Astrophysical Journal* 260 (1982): L75-L78.

11. Ibid.

12. R. A. Fesen, and B. Staker, "The structure and motion of the Crab nebula jet." *Monthly Notices of the Royal Astronomical Society* 263 (1993): 69-74.

13. T. Velusamy, "Radio detection of a jet in the Crab Nebula." *Nature* 308 (1984): 251-252.

14. J. McMoneagle, *The Ultimate Time Machine* (Charlottesville, VA: Hampton Roads, 1999).

15. J. A. West, *Serpent in the Sky: The High Wisdom of Ancient Egypt* (Wheaton, Ill.: Quest, 1993).

16. A. S. Fruchter et al., "The eclipsing millisecond pulsar PSR 1957+20." *The Astrophysical Journal* 351 (1990): 642-650.

7 Natural or Artificial

1. A. Wolszczan, and D. A. Frail, "A planetary system around the millisecond pulsar PSR 1257+12." *Nature* 355 (1992): 145-147.

2. M. Demianski, and M. Prószynski, "Does PSR 0329+54 have companions? *Nature* 282 (1979): 383-385.

3. A. S. Fruchter et al., "The eclipsing millisecond pulsar PSR 1957+20." *The Astrophysical Journal* 351 (1990): 642-650.

4. D. A. Moffet and T. H. Hankins. "Multifrequency radio observations of the Crab pulsar." *Astrophysical Journal* 468 (1996): 779-783.

5. T. H. Hankins, and J. M. Cordes, "Interpulse emission from pulsar 0950+08: How many poles?" *Astrophysical Journal* 249 (1981): 241.

6. S. Johnston et al., "Discovery of a very bright, nearby binary millisecond pulsar." *Nature* 361 (1995): 613-615.

7. D. Backer et al., "A millisecond pulsar." *Nature* 300 (1982):615-620.

8. J. Winn, "The life of a neutron star." *Sky & Telescope*, July 1999, p. 34.

9. N. Bartel, D. Morris, W. Sieber, and T. H. Hankins, "The mode-switching phenomenon in pulsars." *Astrophysical Journal* 258 (1982), p. 777.

10. Ibid.

11. G. R. Huguenin, J. H. Taylor, and T. H. Troland, "The radio emission from pulsar MP 0031-07." *Astrophysical Journal* 162 (1970):727-735.

12. A. V. Filippenko, and V. Radhakrishnan, "Pulsar nulling and drifting subpulse phase memory." *Astrophysical Journal* 263 (1982): 828-834.

13. J. H. Taylor, R. N. Manchester, and G. R. Huguenin, "Observations of pulsar radio emission. I. Total-intensity measurements of individual pulses." *The Astrophysical Journal* 195 (1975): 513-528.

14. J. M. Dawson, "Plasma particle accelerators." *Scientific American*, March 1989, pp. 54-61.

15. P. A. LaViolette, *Subquantum Kinetics: The Alchemy of Creation* (Alexandria, VA: Starlane Publications, 1994), ch. 8.

16. B. Eastlund, "Method and Apparatus for Altering a Region in the Earth's Atmosphere, Ionosphere, and/or Magnetosphere." U.S. patent No. 4,686,605, Aug. 11, 1987.

8 Force Field Beaming Technology

1. T. E. Bearden, *Fer-de-Lance: A Briefing on Soviet Scalar Electromagnetic Weapons* (Ventura, CA: Tesla Book Co., 1986).

2. H. Mason, "Bright Skies: Top-Secret Weapons Testing?" *Nexus* April-May 1997, p. 45.

3. This first hand account was related directly to the Author by these individuals who wished to be known only by their first names.

4. Mason, *Nexus* , pp. 41-47, 78.

5. V. V. Shkunov, and B. Y. Zel'dovich, "Optical phase conjugation." *Scientific American* 253 (December 1985): 54-59.

6. D. M. Pepper, "Applications of optical phase conjugation." *Scientific American* 254 (January 1986): 74-83.

7. Bearden, *Fer-de-Lance.*

8. T. E. Bearden, "Soviet phase conjugate weapons." Bulletin No.

308, Committee to Restore the Constitution, January 1988.

9. P. A. LaViolette, *Beyond the Big Bang: Ancient Myth and the Science of Continuous Creation* (Rochester, Vermont: Park Street Press, 1995).

10. G. Vassilatos, *Secrets of Cold War Technology: Project HAARP and Beyond* (Bayside, CA: Borderland Sciences, 1996), pp. 26-33.

11. Ibid., pp. 51, 55.

12. Ibid., p. 87.

13. R. Zinsser, "Mechanical energy from gravitational anisotropy." trans./ed. T. Valone (Washington, D.C.: Integrity Research Institute, 1989).

14. P. Delgado, and C. Andrews, *Circular Evidence* (London: Bloomsbury Publishing, 1989), pp. 127-128; reprinted by Phanes Press, 1991.

15. Ilyes, *An Hypothesis: The Transmission of a CropCircle*, 1997. On web at: alpha.mic.dundee.ac.uk/ft/crop_circles/ilyes/Abouthy.html.

16. F. Silva, "Music in the Fields." *Atlantis Rising* No. 14 (1998): 42-43.

17. W. C. Levengood, *Physiologia Plantarum* 92 (1994): 356-363.

18. R. Russell, "Report on preliminary results of electrostatic energy testing in crop formations." Midwest Research, Aurora, Colorado, August 1999.

19. P. Delgado, and C. Andrews, *Circular Evidence*, p. 158.

20. Ilyes, *An Hypothesis: The Transmission of a CropCircle*.

21. D. Higbee, "Crop circles: Real or hoax?" Worldwide web posting at users1.ee.net/pmason/crop-circles.html.

22. P. Delgado, and C. Andrews, *Circular Evidence*, p. 115.

23. P. A. Sturrock et al., "Physical evidence related to UFO reports." *Journal of Scientific Exploration* 12 (1998): 179-229.

24. R. Dutton, Excerpt from story printed in Spring 1996 issue of *Circular*, reprinted in Ilyes, *An Hypothesis: Transmission of a Crop Circle*.

25. Higbee, "Crop circles: Real or hoax?"

26. P. Hill, *Unconventional Flying Objects: A Scientific Analysis* (Charlottesville, VA: Hampton Roads Publishing, 1995), pp. 98-116.

27. Ibid., p. 105.

28. C. Lorenzen, and J. Lorenzen, *UFO: The Whole Story* (New York: Signet Books, 1968), p. 97.

29. B. Steiger, *Alien Meetings* (New York: Ace, 1978).

30. A. Lyne, and F. Graham-Smith, *Pulsar Astronomy* (London: Cambridge University Press, 1998), p. 80.

Appendix A: Galactic Distribution of Pulsars with the Parkes Survey Included

1. Pulsar data is taken from: ftp://pulsar.princeton.edu/pub/catalog/ and http://www.atnf.csiro.au/~pulsar/psr/pmsurv/pmwww/.

2. P. A. LaViolette, *Earth Under Fire: Humanity's Survival of the Apocalypse* (Alexandria, VA: Starlane Publications, 1997), ch. 5.

Appendix B: Ordered Complexity

1. J. H. Taylor, R. N. Manchester, and G. R. Huguenin, "Observations of pulsar radio emission. I. Total-intensity measurements of individual pulses." *Astrophysical Journal* 195 (1975): 513-528.

2. J. D. Biggs, P. M. McCulloch, P. A. Hamilton, R. N. Manchester, and A. G. Lyne, "A study of PSR 0826-34—a remarkable pulsar." *Monthly Notices of Royal Astronomical Society* 215 (1985): 281-294.

3. Ibid., p. 292.

4. Ibid., p. 281.

5. J. H. Taylor, and D. Stinebring, "Recent progress in the understanding of pulsars." *Annual Reviews of Astronomy and Astrophysics* 24 (1986): 285-327.

6. G. A. E. Wright, and L. A. Fowler, "Mode-changing and quantized subpulse drift-rates in pulsar PSR 2319+60." *Astronomy and Astrophysics* 101 (1981): 356-361.

Bibliography

Alcubierre, M. "The warp drive: Hyperfast travel within general relativity" *Classic and Quantum Gravity* 11 (1994): L73.

Backer, D. C. "Pulsar fluctuation spectra and the generalized drifting subpulse phenomenon." *The Astrophysical Journal* 182 (1973): 245-276.

Backer, D. C., et al. "A millisecond pulsar." *Nature* 300 (1982): 615-620.

Bartel, N., D. Morris, W. Sieber, and T. H. Hankins. "The mode-switching phenomenon in pulsars." *The Astrophysical Journal* 258 (1982): 776-789."

Bearden, T. E. *Fer-de-Lance: A Briefing on Soviet Scalar Electromagnetic Weapons.* Ventura, CA, Tesla Book Co., 1986.

———. "Soviet phase conjugate weapons." Bulletin No. 308, Committee to Restore the Constitution, January 1988.

Beer, J., et al. "^{10}Be measurements on polar ice: Comparison of Arctic and Antarctic records." *Nuclear Instruments and Methods in Physics Research*, B29 (1987): 203-206.

Beer, J., et al. "^{10}Be peaks as time markers in polar ice cores." In *The Last Deglaciation: Absolute and Radiocarbon Chronologies*, Proc. NATO ASI Series, vol. 12, 140-153. Heidelberg: Springer-Verlag, 1992.

Biggs, J. D., P. M. McCulloch, P. A. Hamilton, R. N. Manchester, and A. G. Lyne. "A study of PSR 0826-34—a remarkable pulsar." *Monthly Notices of Royal Astronomical Society* 215 (1985): 281-294.

Bignami, G. F., and P. A. Caraveo. "On the birthplace of PSR 0833-45: Or, is the Vela pulsar associated with the Vela SNR?" *The Astrophysical Journal* 325 (1988): L5-L7.

Boeckl, B. S. "A depth profile of ^{14}C in the lunar rock 12002." *Earth and Planetary Science Letters* 16 (1972): 269-272.

Bower, G. , H. Falcke, and D. C. Backer. "Circular polarization in Sagittarius A*." 195th American Astronomical Society meeting, Atlanta, GA, January 2000.

Briggs, J., and D. Peat. *Turbulent Mirror.* San Francisco: Harper & Row, 1989, pp. 97-101.

Brown, T. T. "How I control gravity." *Science and Invention magazine*, August 1929.

———. "Electrogravitational communication system." patent disclosure, Sept. 1953; available at http://www.soteria.com.

Cady, W. M. "An investigation relative to Thomas Townsend Brown." Office of Naval Research, Pasadena, June 1952, p. 3.

Clark, D. H., and J. L. Caswell. "A study of Galactic supernova remnants based on Molonglo-Parkes observational data." *Monthly Notices of the Royal Astronomical Society* 174 (1996): 267-305.

Cocke, W. J., M. Disney, G. Muncaster, and T. Gehrels. "Optical polarization of the Crab Nebula pulsar." *Nature* 227 (1970): 1327-1329.

Cornille, P. "Review of the application of Newton's third law in physics." *Progress in Energy and Combustion Science* 25 (1999): 161-210.

Dawson, J. M. "Plasma particle accelerators." *Scientific American*, March 1989, pp. 54-61.

Dea, J. "Instantaneous interactions." Proceedings of the 1986 International Tesla Symposium, Colorado Springs, CO: International Tesla Soc., 1986, p. 4-39.

Delgado, P. and C. Andrews. *Circular Evidence.* London: Bloomsbury Publishing, 1989, reprinted by Phanes Press, 1991.

Demianski, M., and M. Prószynski. "Does PSR 0329+54 have companions? *Nature* 282 (1979): 383-385.

Dewey, R. J., J. H. Taylor, C. M. Maguire, and G. H. Stokes. "Period derivatives and improved parameters for 66 pulsars." *The Astrophysical Journal* 332 (1988): 762-769.

Dickel, J. R., and E. W. Greisen. "The evolution of the radio emission from Cas A." *Astronomy and Astrophysics* 75 (1979): 44-53.

Enders, A. and G. Nimtz. "On superluminal barrier traversal." *Physical Review* E 48 (1993): 632.

Erickson, W. C., et al. "Very long baseline interferometer observations of Taurus A and other sources at 121.6 MHz." *Astrophysical Journal* 177 (1972): 101.

Fesen, R. A. and B. Staker. "The structure and motion of the Crab nebula jet." *Monthly Notices of the Royal Astronomical Society* 263 (1993): 69-74.

Filippenko, A. V., and V. Radhakrishnan. "Pulsar nulling and drifting subpulse phase memory." *Astrophysical Journal* 263 (1982): 828-834.

Fowler, L. A., G. A. E. Wright, and D. Morris. "Unusual properties of the pulsar PSR 1822-09." *Astronomy & Astrophysics* 93 (1981): 54-61.

Fruchter, A. S., et al. "The eclipsing millisecond pulsar PSR 1957+20." *The Astrophysical Journal* 351 (1990): 642-650.

Gold, T. "Rotating neutron stars as the origin of the pulsating radio sources." *Nature* 218 (1968): 731-732.

——. "Apollo II observations of a remarkable glazing phenomenon on the lunar surface." *Science* 165 (1969): 1345-1349.

Gower, J. , and E. Argyle. "Detection of strong interpulses from NP

0532." *The Astrophysical Journal* 171 (1972): L23-L26.

Gull, T. R., and R. A. Fesen. "Deep optical imagery of the Crab Nebula's jet." *The Astrophysical Journal* 260 (1982): L75-L78.

Hankins, T. H. "Microsecond intensity variations in the radio emissions from CP 0950." *The Astrophysical Journal* 169 (1971): 487-494.

Hankins, T. H., and J. M. Cordes. "Interpulse emission from pulsar 0950+08: How many poles?" *The Astrophysical Journal* 249 (1981): 241.

Hankins, T. H., and D. A. Moffet. "Multifrequency radio observations of the Crab pulsar." *The Astrophysical Journal* 468 (1996): 779-783.

Harnden, F. R. "Einstein observations of the Crab nebula pulsar." *The Astrophysical Journal* 283 (1984): 279-285.

Heiles, C., D. B. Campbell, and J. M. Rankin. "Pulsar NP 0532: Properties and systematic polarization of individual strong pulses at 430 MHz." *Nature* 226 (1970): 529-531.

Hewish, A., S. Bell, J. Pilkington, P. Scott, and R. Collins. "Observation of a rapidly pulsating radio source." *Nature* 217 (1968): 709-713.

Hill, P. *Unconventional Flying Objects: A Scientific Analysis.* Charlottesville, VA: Hampton Roads Publishing, 1995, p. 98.

Hughen, K. A., et al. "Deglacial changes in ocean circulation from an extended radiocarbon calibration." *Nature* 391 (1998): 65-68.

Huguenin, G. R., J. H. Taylor, and T. H. Troland. "The radio emission from pulsar MP 0031-07." *The Astrophysical Journal* 162 (1970): 727-735.

Ilyes. *An Hypothesis: The Transmission of a CropCircle*, 1997. http://alpha.mic.dundee.ac. uk /ft/crop_circles/ilyes/Abouthy.html.

Intel. "Towards flight without stress or strain... or weight." *Interavia* il(5) (1956): 373-374.

Isaacman, R. "NP0532 and a hole in the Crab Nebula." *Nature* 268 (1977): 317-318.

Ishii, T. K., and G. C. Giakos. "Radio Messages Faster Than Light." *Microwaves & RF* 30, Aug. 1991, pp 114-119.

———. "Rapid Pulsed Microwave Propagation." *IEEE Microwave & Guided Wave Letters* 1(12), Dec. 1991, pp 374-375

Jastrow, R., and M. H. Thompson. *Astronomy: Fundamentals and Frontiers.* New York: John Wiley & Sons, 1977, p. 198.

Johnston, S. "Evidence for a deficit of pulsars in the inner Galaxy." *Monthly Notices of the Royal Astronomical Society* 268 (1994): 595-601.

Johnston, S., et al. "Discovery of a very bright, nearby binary millisecond pulsar." *Nature* 361 (1995): 613-615.

Jouzel, J., et al. "Vostok ice core: A continuous isotope temperature record over the last climatic cycle (160,000 years)." *Nature* 329 (1987): 403-408.

Kanbach, G., et al. "Detailed characteristics of the high-energy gamma radiation from PSR 0833-45 measured by COS-B." *Astronomy and Astrophysics* 90 (1980): 163-169.

Kulkarni, S. R., and J. J. Hester. "Discovery of a nebula around PSR 1957+20." *Nature* 335 (1988): 801-804.

LaViolette, P. A. Galactic Explosions, Cosmic Dust Invasions and Climatic Change. Ph.D. dissertation, Portland State Univ., Portland, OR, 1983, 763 pp.

————. "Cosmic-ray volleys from the Galactic Center and their recent impact on the Earth environment." *Earth Moon Planets* 37 (1987): 241-286.

————. "A Tesla wave physics for a free energy universe." Proceedings of the 1990 International Tesla Symposium, pp. 5.1-5.19. Colorado Springs, CO: International Tesla Society, 1991.

————. "The planetary-stellar mass-luminosity relation: Possible evidence of energy nonconservation?" *Physics Essays* 5 (4) (1992): 536-544.

————. *Subquantum Kinetics: The Alchemy of Creation.* Alexandria, VA: Starlane Publications, 1994.

————. "The U.S. Antigravity Squadron." in *Electrogravitics Systems: Reports on a New Propulsion Methodology,* edited by T. Valone. Washington, D.C.: Integrity Research Institute, 1994.

————. *Beyond the Big Bang: Ancient Myth and the Science of Continuous Creation.* Rochester, Vermont: Park Street Press, 1995.

————. *Earth Under Fire: Humanity's Survival of the Apocalypse.* Alexandria, VA: Starlane Publications, 1997.

————. "Global warming at the Termination I boundary: Part I. Supporting evidence and the inadequacy of terrestrial climate change mechanisms." 1999 (submitted for journal publication).

————. "Global warming at the Termination I boundary: Part II. An extraterrestrial cause." 1999 (submitted for journal publication).

Levengood, W. C. *Physiologia Plantarum* 92 (1994): 356-363.

Lorenzen, C., and J. Lorenzen. *UFO: The Whole Story.* New York: Signet, 1968.

Lyne, A. G., and F. Graham-Smith. *Pulsar Astronomy.* London: Cambridge University Press, 1998.

Lyne, A. G., R. S. Pritchard, F. Graham-Smith, and F. Camilo. "Very low braking index for the Vela pulsar." *Nature* 381 (1996): 497-498.

Manchester, R. N., J. H. Taylor, and G. R. Huguenin. "Observations of pulsar radio emission. II. Polarization of individual pulses." *The Astrophysical Journal* 196 (1975): 83-112.

Manchester, R. N., and J. H. Taylor. "Recent Observations of Pulsars."

Annual Reviews of Astronomy and Astrophysics 15 (1977): 19-44.

————. "Observed and derived parameters for 330 pulsars." *The Astronomical Journal* 86 (1981): 1953-1973.

Mason, H. "Bright Skies: Top-Secret Weapons Testing?" *Nexus* April-May 1997, pp. 41-47, 78.

McCulloch, P. M., P. A. Hamilton, G. W. R. Royle, and R. N. Manchester. "Daily observations of a large period jump of the Vela pulsar." *Nature* 302 (1983): 319-321.

McMoneagle, J. *The Ultimate Time Machine* Charlottesville, VA: Hampton Roads, 1999.

Michanowsky, G. *The Once and Future Star*. New York: Barnes and Noble, 1979.

Misner, C., K. Thorne, and J. A. Wheeler. *Gravitation* San Francisco: Freeman and Co., 1973.

Moffet, D. A., and T. H. Hankins. "Multifrequency radio observations of the Crab pulsar." *The Astrophysical Journal* 468 (1996): 779-783.

Ögelman, H., L. Koch-Miramond, and M. Auriére. "Measurement of the Vela pulsar's proper motion and detection of the optical counterpart of its compact X-ray nebula." *The Astrophysical Journal* 342 (1989): L83-L86.

Pepper, D. M. "Applications of optical phase conjugation." *Scientific American* 254 (January 1986): 74-83.

Plutarch. "Lucullus." in *Plutarch's Lives* vol. 2, translated by B. Perrin, pp. 495-497. Cambridge, MA: Harvard University Press, 1968.

Preston, R. "The eclipsing death star." *Discovery*, Aug. 1988, pp. 41-46.

Puthoff, H. "SETI, the velocity-of-light limitation, and the Alcubierre warp drive: An integrating overview." *Physics Essays* 9 (1996): 156.

Raisbeck, G. M., et al. "^{10}Be deposition at Vostok, Antarctica during the last 50,000 years and its relationship to possible cosmogenic production variations during this period." In *The Last Deglaciation: Absolute and Radiocarbon Chronologies* (Proc. NATO ASI Series, vol. 12), edited by E. Bard and W. Broecker, pp. 127-139. Heidelberg: Springer-Verlag, 1992.

Reynolds, S. P., and D. C. Ellison. "Electron acceleration in Tycho's and Kepler's supernova remnants: Spectral evidence of Fermi shock acceleration." *The Astrophysical Journal* 399 (1992): L75-L78.

Schmidt, G. D., J. Angel, and E. Beaver. "The small-scale polarization of the Crab Nebula." *Astrophysical Journal* 227 (1979): 106-113.

Sharp, N. A. "Millisecond time resolution with the Kitt Peak Photoncounting array." *Publications of the Astronomical Society of the Pacific* 104 (1992): 263-269.

Shkunov, V. V. and B. Y. Zel'dovich. "Optical phase conjugation." *Scientific American* 253 (December 1985): 54-59.

Silva, F. "Music in the Fields." *Atlantis Rising* No. 14 (1998): 42-43.

Steiger, B. *Alien Meetings*. New York: Ace, 1978.

Sturrock, P. A., et al. "Physical evidence related to UFO reports." *Journal of Scientific Exploration* 12 (1998): 179-229.

Sullivan, W. *Black Holes*. Garden City, NY: Anchor Press, 1979.

Taylor, J. H., R. N. Manchester, and G. R. Huguenin. "Observations of pulsar radio emission. I. Total-intensity measurements of individual pulses." *The Astrophysical Journal* 195 (1975): 513-528.

Taylor, J. H., R. N. Manchester, and A. G. Lyne. "Catalog of 558 pulsars." *Astrophysical Journal Supplement Series* 88 (1993): 529-568.

Taylor, J. H., and D. R. Stinebring. "Recent progress in the understanding of pulsars." *Annual Reviews Astronomy and Astrophysics* 24 (1986): 285-327.

Thompson, R. L. *Alien Identities: Ancient Insights into Modern UFO Phenomena*. San Diego, CA: Govardhan Hill Publishing, 1993.

Trimble, V. "Motions and Structure of the Filamentary Envelope of the Crab Nebula." *Astronomical Journal* 73 (1968): 535-547.

Tucker, W. H. "Supernova in the sail." *Star and Sky* 2(1) (1980): 36.

Vassilatos, G. *Secrets of Cold War Technology: Project HAARP and Beyond*. Bayside, CA: Borderland Sciences, 1996.

Velusamy, T. "Radio detection of a jet in the Crab Nebula." *Nature* 308 (1984): 251-252.

Wallace, H. W. "Method and apparatus for generating a secondary gravitational force field." U.S. patent No. 3,626,605, Dec. 14, 1971.

———. "Method and apparatus for generating a dynamic force field." U.S. patent No. 3,626,606, Dec. 14, 1971.

Wilson, R. B., and G. J. Fishman. "The pulse profile of the Crab pulsar in the energy range 45 keV - 1.2 Mev." *The Astrophysical Journal* 269 (1983): 273-280.

Winn, J. "The life of a neutron star." *Sky & Telescope*, July 1999, p. 34.

Wolszczan, A., and D. A. Frail. "A planetary system around the millisecond pulsar PSR 1257+12." *Nature* 355 (1992): 145-147.

Woodward, J. "A new experimental approach to Mach's principle and relativistic gravitation." *Foundations of Physics Letters*, vol. 3(5), 1990.

Wright, G. A. E., and L. A. Fowler. "Mode-changing and quantized subpulse drift-rates in pulsar PSR 2319+60." *Astronomy and Astrophysics* 101 (1981): 356-361.

Zinsser, R. "Mechanical energy from gravitational anisotropy." edited by T. Valone. Washington, D.C.: Integrity Research Institute, 1989.

Zook, H. A., J. B. Hartung, and D. Storzer. "Solar flare activity: Evidence for large-scale changes in the past." *Icarus* 32 (1977): 106-126.

Index

accelerator, particle, 4, 120-121, 126, 173

ages, zodiacal, 90-91

Alexander, Steven, 145

Andrews, Colin, 138, 141, 143-144

Arecibo radio telescope, 21, 26

Astraea, myth of, 92

astrological star lore. *See* constellation star lore

Barrett, Alan, 3

beacons, ETI, 2, 15-17, 25, 28, 32-33, 80, 121-124, 162
  as markers, 36-39, 57, 63, 65, 70
  as warning indicators, 73-75, 86
  See also ETI communication transmitters, navigation beacons

Bearden, Tom, 134-135

Bell, Jocelyn, 1, 7-8, 159

beryllium–10 in polar ice. *See* cosmic ray particles, terrestrial exposure

Beyond the Big Bang, 48, 124,

Bölling interstadial, 85

bow shock front. *See* shock front

Brown, T. Townsend, 30, 34-35

bull, celestial, 88-89, 96

burning of the world.
  See conflagration

carbon–14, excess levels of, 54, 92

catastrophes, global, 48, 51-58, 60-61, 73, 88-89, 92

Centaurus constellation, 48, 96, 149

climatic change, 48, 51-54, 85

Cocke, William, 72

communication, interstellar, 3, 16-17, 23, 29, 50, 57, 77, 80, 110, 115, 117, 166
  beacons. *See* beacons, ETI
  Galactic benchmarks, 24
  network, 3, 28-33, 46, 58, 126
  superluminal, 33-35, 58, 96
  See also beacons, ETI communication transmitters

conflagration, 92

constellations.
  See zodiac constellations

contact, ETI. *See* ETI contact

constellation star lore,
  as a cipher, 48, 58, 84
  encoding science of creation, 48
  galactic core explosion message, 40, 48, 57-58

cosmic dust, 148-149
  activating the Sun and stars, 51-54, 66, 85, 92, 153
  and climatic change, 52-55, 85, 153

cosmic microwave background radiation, 59

cosmic ray particles, 4-5, 16, 125
  distant penetration of, 50-51
  illuminating SNRs, 66-67, 70-71, 87, 149
  light–speed travel through Galaxy, 50, 66, 69, 71
  terrestrial exposure record, 52-57, 85

Crab Nebula. *See* supernova remnants

Crab pulsar. *See* pulsars

crop circles, 138-149

Crucis constellation, 44, 48, 57
  See also one–radian markers

Delgado, Pat, 141-142

Drake, Frank, 6, 15

Earth Under Fire, 48, 69, 88

EBM Pulsar. *See* pulsars

eccentricity, orbital, 42, 101

Egyptian New Year, 91 fn

energy/matter creation, 48-49

equinox, as time indicator, 90-92

ETI communication beacons. *See* beacons, ETI

ETI communication transmitters
  engineered stellar cores, 16-17, 39, 123-127
  particle beam communicator, 4-5, 120-123, 173-174

ETI contact, 149-150
    in ancient times, 46, 58-59, 97-98
explosions, galactic.
    See Galactic core explosions
extinction, mass animal, 54, 61, 85
    92-93
extraterrestrial communication,
    See communication, interstellar

Fesen, Robert, 94
Fillippenko, Alexei, 118
force field beaming technology, 16,
    128-148

galactic anticenter, 64, 70, 79, 87-88
Galactic center, 18-24 27, 40, 95
    as reference location, 18-20, 24-25,
        28, 41, 44-46, 57-58
    as site of matter-energy creation
        and expulsion, 40, 42, 48-50,
        66-70, 84, 88, 96
    See also one-radian markers,
    Sagittarius constellation
Galactic commune, 3
Galactic core explosions, 28, 40, 50,
    56
    cyclic recurrence of, 52-56
    See also Galactic center, superwaves
Galactic core. *See* Galactic center
Galactic internet, 126
galactic radio background radiation,
    67, 87
Galactic superwave. *See* superwave
galactic plane, 46, 67, 87-88
Galaxy
    distribution of pulsars in, 20-27
    other civilizations in, 3, 15, 23,
        28-30. 35, 46, 50, 57-58, 93
Gamma Sagittae. *See* Sagitta
    constellation
GE Research Laboratory, 4
geomagnetic field disturbances, 92
giant pulses. *See* pulse, giant
glacial growth, melting and recession,
    52, 85, 92
Glastonbury, Peter, 145
glitch. *See* period glitch
Gold, Thomas, 8, 13
gravity control engineering, 29-30
    See *also* spacecraft propulsion
Great Cycle, 90-92

Gull, Theodore, 93

HAARP project, 127
Hankins, Timothy, 104
Hein, Simeon, 143
Hewish, Anthony, 1, 7-8
Higbee, 144
Huguenin, G., 119

ice ages, initiation and termination of,
    52, 60-61
ice core records. *See* beryllium-10
Ilyes, 142
IMPATT diodes, 137
integrated pulse profile. *See* pulse,
    time-averaged profile
interpulses. *See* pulse
interstellar
    communication. *See* communication
    dust. *See* cosmic dust
    radio wave scattering, 6

Jastrow, Robert, 3

Levengood, W. C., 142
lighthouse model,
    See neutron star lighthouse model
longitudinal waves, 34-35
luminous wisps. *See* supernova
    remnants, Crab Nebula wisps
lunar rocks, 53-54, 92

Manchester, Richard, 119, 163
mass extinction episode.
    See extinctions, mass animal
matter-energy creation.
    See energy/matter creation
microwave,
    background radiation. See cosmic
    beam technology, 130-138, 142, 145
        -148
    beam weapons, 128-131
    force-induction by, 135-138, 144-
        149
    phase conjugation of, 131-138
    superluminal waves, 33
Milky Way. *See* Galaxy
Millisecond Pulsar. *See* pulsars
mode switching. *See* pulse
Moffett, David, 104

navigation beacons, 18, 30-33, 150

neutron star lighthouse model,
difficulties of, 7-15, 79-80, 100-
111, 115-119, 124-125, 154-155,
163-164, 168
like the epicycle theory, 119

neutron stars. *See* stars, neutron

one–radian markers, 18, 22-25, 36,
44, 47-50, 99

optical pulses, 38-39, 61, 67, 72-
77, 104-106

Orion constellation, 89, 96

particle beam technology. *See* ETI
communication transmitters

period glitch, 77-80, 90

period-constancy problem, 108-109

phase–conjugation. *See* microwave,
phase conjugation of

Pioneer 10 space plaque, 18-19, 31

plasmoid, 128-135. *See also*
microwave beam technology

Pleistocene, terminal extinction. *See*
extinction

polar ice. *See* beryllium–10 record

polar precession. *See* equinox

Project Centaur, 148-149

Project OZMA, 6, 15

pulsars,
as communication beacons, 2-3,
15-17, 23-28, 39, 41, 59, 77,
80, 86, 106-126
Crab pulsar, 60-90, 100, 102-106,
109-110, 116, 122, 150-151
discovery of, 1-3, 7
Eclipsing Binary Millisecond
(EBM) Pulsar, 41-47, 98-101,
107-109
highly ordered emission, 14-15,
110-119
lighthouse model. *See* neutron star
Millisecond Pulsar, 36-40, 42, 47,
50, 75-77, 87, 99, 107-109
natural pulsating sources, 111
nonrandomly distributed, 19-28,
41, 44-46, 63, 78-79, 90
PSR 0525+21, 80, 89-90
stationary-beam model. *See* ETI
communication transmitters
Vela pulsar, 60-64, 73-86, 98-
100, 104-106, 151, 164

Vulpecula pulsar, 40-41, 46, 81-
86, 100

pulse,
complexity, 14-15, 110-119
drifting, 14, 112, 114-118, 160-
164, 168-172
freezing, 112, 115, 163, 172
giant, 38, 76-77
interpulse, 61, 75-77, 102-106,
166-168
mode switching, 112, 115-118,
121, 126, 164-172
quantized, 117-118, 168-171
grammar, 117-118, 169-171
modulation, 111-116, 158-160,
164-165
nulling, 112, 115, 117-118, 161-
163, 169-172
period, 2, 11, 37-39, 42-43, 77-86
period derivative, 16, 82-85, 112
scattering. *See* interstellar
scattering
subpulse, 10 fn, 118, 154, 163
time-averaged profile, 10-14, 39,
111-112
variability, 13, 111, 150

Radhakrishnan, V., 118

radian, 22. *See also* one–radian marker

radio telescope,
Arecibo, 20-21, 26
Jodrell Bank, 21
Green Bank, 6, 21
Parkes, 46, 152-153

radio transmissions,
broadband, 3, 5-6
discrete frequency, 3, 5-6

radiocarbon levels. *See* carbon-14

remote viewing, 97, 150

Russell, Ron, 143

Ryle, Martin, 7

Sagitta constellation, 24, 39-41, 44-
49, 57-58, 81-87, 98
Gamma Sagittae, 40, 46, 82-83, 99
See also one–radian markers

Sagittarius constellation,
arrow of, 44, 48-49, 57, 84
shooting at Scorpius, 48
See also Galactic center

scalar waves, 135

Scorpius constellation, 44, 49

SETI, 3, 6, 15, 29, 117, 150, 166
shield,
    force field, 93-96, 128, 138, 148
    of Centaurus, 96
    of Orion, 89, 96
shock front, bow, 71-74, 107-108
solar conflagration, 92-93
    as cause of Pleistocene extinction,
        54, 85-86, 92
    evidence of solar flare activity, 53-
        54, 92
    evidence in moon rocks, 53-54, 92
solar wind,
    screening out cosmic rays, 53-56
Sothic calendar, 91
Southern Cross. *See* Crucis
space navigation, 30-33
spacecraft propulsion, 29-30, 136,
    145-148
Staker, Bryan, 94
Starburst Foundation, 148
stars,
    dust accretion by, 51, 66, 92
    dust cocoon around, 51
    neutron, 2, 7-9, 27, 62, 107-110,
        114-117, 124
    neutron star pancake model, 8
    white dwarf, 2, 8, 16-17, 101,
        107-111, 123-125, 164
stationary-beam transmitter. *See* ETI
    communication transmitters
Stinebring, Dan, 42, 62
subquantum kinetics, 30, 124, 136
Sun, aggravated by dust, 54, 85, 92
superluminal, communication. *See*
    communication, extraterrestrial
superluminal space travel, 29-30
supernova remnants, 5, 27
    Cassiopeia A, 68-69, 73-74
    cosmic ray trapping by, 5, 67-68,
        71-73
    Crab Nebula, 8, 38, 60-69, 71-72,
        86-97, 110
        as superwave scale model, 86-88
        jet, 93-96, 148
        magnetic field, 72-73
        wisps, 71-72
    North Polar Spur, 63, 153
    Tycho, 68-70, 73
    Vela, 8, 60-66, 73

subpulse. *See* pulse
supernovae,
    Crab, 60-67, 70, 86-88, 93, 97
    triggered by superwaves, 68-70
    ETI engineered, 88-90, 95
    Vela, 61-66, 69-70, 77, 88, 100
superwave, 50-59, 65-77, 84-98,
    150-153
    cosmic rays, 71
    defense against, 96, 128, 138, 148-
        149
    event horizon, 68-74, 77, 84, 86-90,
        150
    in other galaxies, 50, 57
    See also Galactic core explosions
synchrotron radiation, 4, 5, 8-13, 16-
    17, 51, 56, 67-69, 71-73, 87, 95
    circularly polarized, 51, 155
    produced by superwaves, 56-57,
        67-73, 86-88, 95
    from pulsars, 5-9, 16-17, 102,
        106, 120-127

talk of the Galaxy, 50, 57
Taurus constellation, 32, 60, 88-89
Taylor, Joseph, 62, 119
Terminal Pleistocene Extinction. *See*
    extinction
Tesla, Nikola, 35, 135-137
Tesla waves, 136, 138, 146, 150
Thomas, M., 3
time-averaged pulse profile. *See* pulse
Tycho remnant. *See* supernova
    remnants

Vela. *See* pulsars, supernova remnants
vernal equinox, precession of, 91-92
Virgo,
    constellation, 59
    -Leo ecliptic marker, 92
Vostok, East Antarctica ice record,
    54-55
Vulpecula pulsar. *See* pulsars
Woodward, James, 147 fn

Zinsser, Rudolph, 137, 142
zodiac constellations (astrological)
    conveying ancient message, 48-
        49, 58, 84
zodiac star chronometer, 84